Practice Workbook

ON MY OWN

TEACHER'S EDITION
Grade 2

Harcourt Brace & Company

Orlando • Atlanta • Austin • Boston • San Francisco • Chicago • Dallas • New York • Toronto • London

http://www.hbschool.com

CONTENTS

Name _____

Sums to 10

▶ **Vocabulary**

Check children's work.

Circle the **addends** .
Circle the **sums** .

1. $6 + 2 = 8$ $5 + 4 = 9$ $7 + 3 = 10$

Write the sum.

2.

$4 + 3 = \underline{7}$

3.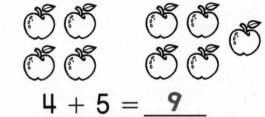

$4 + 5 = \underline{9}$

4.

$5 + 1 = \underline{6}$

5.

$3 + 2 = \underline{5}$

6.

$7 + 3 = \underline{10}$

7.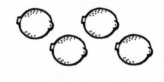

$4 + 2 = \underline{6}$

▶ **Problem Solving**

Write the addition sentence.

8. Jan collected 4 shells.
David collected 6 shells.
How many shells do
they have in all?

$\underline{4} + \underline{6} = \underline{10}$
shells

9. Tracy picked 7 flowers.
Albert picked 1 flower.
How many flowers do
they have in all?

$\underline{7} + \underline{1} = \underline{8}$
flowers

Harcourt Brace School Publishers

Order Property

Write the sum.

1.

$4 + 3 =$ __7__ $9 + 1 =$ __10__ $2 + 6 =$ __8__

$3 + 4 =$ __7__ $1 + 9 =$ __10__ $6 + 2 =$ __8__

2.

$5 + 4 =$ __9__ $3 + 5 =$ __8__ $6 + 1 =$ __7__

$4 + 5 =$ __9__ $5 + 3 =$ __8__ $1 + 6 =$ __7__

3.

$$\begin{array}{r} 3 \\ + 2 \\ \hline 5 \end{array} \qquad \begin{array}{r} 2 \\ + 3 \\ \hline 5 \end{array} \qquad \begin{array}{r} 8 \\ + 1 \\ \hline 9 \end{array} \qquad \begin{array}{r} 1 \\ + 8 \\ \hline 9 \end{array} \qquad \begin{array}{r} 4 \\ + 6 \\ \hline 10 \end{array} \qquad \begin{array}{r} 6 \\ + 4 \\ \hline 10 \end{array}$$

4.

$$\begin{array}{r} 1 \\ + 7 \\ \hline 8 \end{array} \qquad \begin{array}{r} 7 \\ + 1 \\ \hline 8 \end{array} \qquad \begin{array}{r} 4 \\ + 2 \\ \hline 6 \end{array} \qquad \begin{array}{r} 2 \\ + 4 \\ \hline 6 \end{array} \qquad \begin{array}{r} 7 \\ + 2 \\ \hline 9 \end{array} \qquad \begin{array}{r} 2 \\ + 7 \\ \hline 9 \end{array}$$

▶ Problem Solving

Write the addition sentence.

5. Emilio has 3 red pencils and 2 blue pencils. How many pencils does he have in all?

__3__ + __2__ = __5__
pencils

6. Pat has 7 red pencils and 3 blue pencils. How many pencils does she have in all?

__7__ + __3__ = __10__
pencils

Zero Property

Write the sum.

1.

$5 + 0 = \underline{5}$ $0 + 7 = \underline{7}$ $0 + 9 = \underline{9}$

2.

$0 + 3 = \underline{3}$ $6 + 0 = \underline{6}$ $8 + 0 = \underline{8}$

3.

$$\begin{array}{r} 9 \\ + 0 \\ \hline 9 \end{array} \qquad \begin{array}{r} 0 \\ + 7 \\ \hline 7 \end{array} \qquad \begin{array}{r} 8 \\ + 0 \\ \hline 8 \end{array} \qquad \begin{array}{r} 1 \\ + 0 \\ \hline 1 \end{array}$$

4.

$$\begin{array}{r} 6 \\ + 0 \\ \hline 6 \end{array} \qquad \begin{array}{r} 0 \\ + 2 \\ \hline 2 \end{array} \qquad \begin{array}{r} 5 \\ + 0 \\ \hline 5 \end{array} \qquad \begin{array}{r} 4 \\ + 0 \\ \hline 4 \end{array}$$

▶ **Problem Solving**

Draw a picture. Then write the addition sentence.

5. Suki has 5 bananas and Jim has none. How many bananas do they have in all?

$\underline{5} + \underline{0} = \underline{5}$
bananas

Counting On

Count on to find the sum.

1.

$8 + 1 = \underline{9}$ $5 + 2 = \underline{7}$ $3 + 3 = \underline{6}$

2.

$4 + 1 = \underline{5}$ $6 + 2 = \underline{8}$ $7 + 3 = \underline{10}$

3.

$$\begin{array}{r} 3 \\ + 1 \\ \hline 4 \end{array} \qquad \begin{array}{r} 8 \\ + 2 \\ \hline 10 \end{array} \qquad \begin{array}{r} 7 \\ + 2 \\ \hline 9 \end{array} \qquad \begin{array}{r} 7 \\ + 3 \\ \hline 10 \end{array} \qquad \begin{array}{r} 5 \\ + 1 \\ \hline 6 \end{array} \qquad \begin{array}{r} 6 \\ + 1 \\ \hline 7 \end{array}$$

4.

$$\begin{array}{r} 4 \\ + 3 \\ \hline 7 \end{array} \qquad \begin{array}{r} 2 \\ + 1 \\ \hline 3 \end{array} \qquad \begin{array}{r} 9 \\ + 1 \\ \hline 10 \end{array} \qquad \begin{array}{r} 6 \\ + 3 \\ \hline 9 \end{array} \qquad \begin{array}{r} 4 \\ + 2 \\ \hline 6 \end{array} \qquad \begin{array}{r} 5 \\ + 3 \\ \hline 8 \end{array}$$

5.

$$\begin{array}{r} 3 \\ + 2 \\ \hline 5 \end{array} \qquad \begin{array}{r} 8 \\ + 1 \\ \hline 9 \end{array} \qquad \begin{array}{r} 5 \\ + 2 \\ \hline 7 \end{array} \qquad \begin{array}{r} 6 \\ + 2 \\ \hline 8 \end{array} \qquad \begin{array}{r} 4 \\ + 1 \\ \hline 5 \end{array} \qquad \begin{array}{r} 7 \\ + 1 \\ \hline 8 \end{array}$$

▶ **Problem Solving**

Draw 2 eggs. Count on to find the sum.

6. A hen laid 4 eggs. The next day it laid 2 more. How many eggs did the hen lay in all?

_____6_____ eggs

Addition Practice

Write the sum.

1.

$7 + 3 =$ __10__ $8 + 2 =$ __10__

2.

$5 + 3 =$ __8__ $6 + 3 =$ __9__

3.
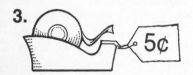

$$\begin{array}{r} 5\,¢ \\ +\ 4\,¢ \\ \hline 9\,¢ \end{array}$$

$$\begin{array}{r} 8\,¢ \\ +\ 2\,¢ \\ \hline 10\,¢ \end{array}$$

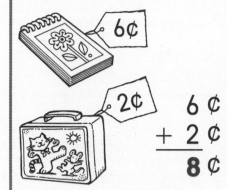

$$\begin{array}{r} 6\,¢ \\ +\ 2\,¢ \\ \hline 8\,¢ \end{array}$$

4.

$$\begin{array}{r} 7\,¢ \\ +\ 2\,¢ \\ \hline 9\,¢ \end{array}$$

$$\begin{array}{r} 9\,¢ \\ +\ 1\,¢ \\ \hline 10\,¢ \end{array}$$

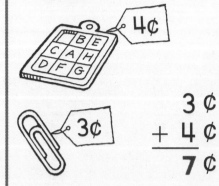

$$\begin{array}{r} 3\,¢ \\ +\ 4\,¢ \\ \hline 7\,¢ \end{array}$$

5.
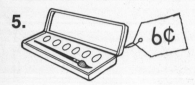

$$\begin{array}{r} 6\,¢ \\ +\ 2\,¢ \\ \hline 8\,¢ \end{array}$$

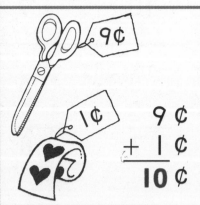

$$\begin{array}{r} 4\,¢ \\ +\ 5\,¢ \\ \hline 9\,¢ \end{array}$$

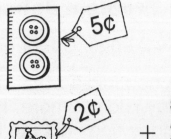

$$\begin{array}{r} 5\,¢ \\ +\ 2\,¢ \\ \hline 7\,¢ \end{array}$$

Differences Through 10

Write the difference.

1.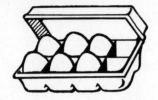

8 − 2 = __6__

2.

10 − 6 = __4__

3.

6 − 2 = __4__

4.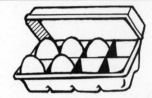

8 − 3 = __5__

5.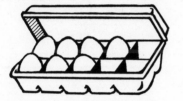

10 − 3 = __7__

6.

6 − 3 = __3__

7.

8 − 6 = __2__

8.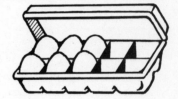

10 − 4 = __6__

▶ **Problem Solving**

Draw a picture to solve.

9. There are 8 muffins on a plate. Claire eats 2. How many muffins are left?

__6__ muffins

Subtracting All or Zero

Subtract.

1. How many flowers are left?

$$\begin{array}{r} 6 \\ -\ 6 \\ \hline 0 \end{array}$$ flowers

How many flowers are left?

$$\begin{array}{r} 6 \\ -\ 0 \\ \hline 6 \end{array}$$ flowers

2.
$$\begin{array}{r} 4 \\ -\ 0 \\ \hline 4 \end{array}$$
$$\begin{array}{r} 2 \\ -\ 2 \\ \hline 0 \end{array}$$
$$\begin{array}{r} 5 \\ -\ 0 \\ \hline 5 \end{array}$$
$$\begin{array}{r} 7 \\ -\ 0 \\ \hline 7 \end{array}$$
$$\begin{array}{r} 9 \\ -\ 9 \\ \hline 0 \end{array}$$

3.
$$\begin{array}{r} 8 \\ -\ 8 \\ \hline 0 \end{array}$$
$$\begin{array}{r} 3 \\ -\ 0 \\ \hline 3 \end{array}$$
$$\begin{array}{r} 6 \\ -\ 6 \\ \hline 0 \end{array}$$
$$\begin{array}{r} 1 \\ -\ 0 \\ \hline 1 \end{array}$$
$$\begin{array}{r} 3 \\ -\ 3 \\ \hline 0 \end{array}$$

4.
$$\begin{array}{r} 9 \\ -\ 0 \\ \hline 9 \end{array}$$
$$\begin{array}{r} 5 \\ -\ 5 \\ \hline 0 \end{array}$$
$$\begin{array}{r} 8 \\ -\ 0 \\ \hline 8 \end{array}$$
$$\begin{array}{r} 2 \\ -\ 0 \\ \hline 2 \end{array}$$
$$\begin{array}{r} 7 \\ -\ 7 \\ \hline 0 \end{array}$$

▶ **Problem Solving**

Write the subtraction sentence.

5. Jessica cut 6 roses. She gave 6 roses to her mother. How many roses does she have left?

___6___ – ___6___ = ___0___ roses

6. Derek put 2 bones in the dog bowl. The dog did not eat the bones. How many bones are left in the bowl?

___2___ – ___0___ = ___2___ bones

Harcourt Brace School Publishers

Using Subtraction to Compare

Compare. Then subtract.

1. ○○○○○○○
   △△△△

   7 − 4 = __3__ more circles

2. △△△△△△△△
   ○○

   8 − 2 = __6__ more triangles

3. △△△△△
   ○○○

   5 − 3 = __2__ more triangles

4. ○○○○○○○○○
   △△△△△△

   9 − 6 = __3__ more circles

5. ○○○○○○
   △△△

   6 − 3 = __3__ more circles

6. ○○○○○○○○
   △△△△△

   8 − 5 = __3__ more circles

7. △△△△△△△△△
   ○○○○

   9 − 4 = __5__ more triangles

8. △△△△△△
   ○○○○○

   6 − 5 = __1__ more triangle

▶ **Problem Solving**

Draw a picture to compare.
Then write the subtraction sentence.

9. Andre has 6 toy boats and
   3 toy cars. How many more
   toy boats does he have?

   __6__ − __3__ = __3__
   more toy boats

Counting Back

Count back to find the difference.

1. $8 - 1 = \underline{7}$ $4 - 2 = \underline{2}$ $6 - 1 = \underline{5}$

2. $5 - 2 = \underline{3}$ $9 - 3 = \underline{6}$ $10 - 2 = \underline{8}$

3.
$$\begin{array}{r} 7 \\ -3 \\ \hline 4 \end{array} \qquad \begin{array}{r} 5 \\ -1 \\ \hline 4 \end{array} \qquad \begin{array}{r} 8 \\ -3 \\ \hline 5 \end{array} \qquad \begin{array}{r} 4 \\ -1 \\ \hline 3 \end{array} \qquad \begin{array}{r} 6 \\ -4 \\ \hline 2 \end{array}$$

4.
$$\begin{array}{r} 10 \\ -4 \\ \hline 6 \end{array} \qquad \begin{array}{r} 9 \\ -3 \\ \hline 6 \end{array} \qquad \begin{array}{r} 5 \\ -4 \\ \hline 1 \end{array} \qquad \begin{array}{r} 7 \\ -2 \\ \hline 5 \end{array} \qquad \begin{array}{r} 3 \\ -2 \\ \hline 1 \end{array}$$

5.
$$\begin{array}{r} 8 \\ -2 \\ \hline 6 \end{array} \qquad \begin{array}{r} 3 \\ -1 \\ \hline 2 \end{array} \qquad \begin{array}{r} 6 \\ -4 \\ \hline 2 \end{array} \qquad \begin{array}{r} 2 \\ -1 \\ \hline 1 \end{array} \qquad \begin{array}{r} 7 \\ -1 \\ \hline 6 \end{array}$$

6.
$$\begin{array}{r} 3 \\ -2 \\ \hline 1 \end{array} \qquad \begin{array}{r} 8 \\ -4 \\ \hline 4 \end{array} \qquad \begin{array}{r} 6 \\ -3 \\ \hline 3 \end{array} \qquad \begin{array}{r} 7 \\ -4 \\ \hline 3 \end{array} \qquad \begin{array}{r} 5 \\ -3 \\ \hline 2 \end{array}$$

▶ **Problem Solving**

Draw a picture to compare.
Then write the subtraction sentence.

7. Niko has 3 brothers and 1 sister.
How many more brothers than
sisters does Niko have?

$\underline{3} - \underline{1} = \underline{2}$
more brothers

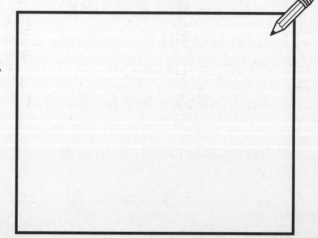

Name _____

Problem Solving • Make a Model

Use the four steps to solve the problem.

1. Julie bought 3 green apples and 5 red apples. How many apples did she buy in all?

   __5__ (+) __3__ = __8__

   __8__ apples

2. Mary has 6 dolls. Tasha has 4 dolls. How many more dolls does Mary have?

   __6__ (−) __4__ = __2__

   __2__ more dolls

3. Joel planted 7 tomato seeds and 2 carrot seeds. How many seeds did he plant in all?

   __7__ (+) __2__ = __9__

   __9__ seeds

4. Eddie had 6 jelly beans. He ate 3 of them. How many jelly beans does he have left?

   __6__ (−) __3__ = __3__

   __3__ jelly beans

Harcourt Brace School Publishers

Doubles

▶ Vocabulary

Circle the **doubles** facts.

1. (1 + 1 = 2)   4 + 3 = 7   (6 + 6 = 12)

Write the sum.

2. 3 + 3 = __6__   8 + 8 = __16__   6 + 6 = __12__

3. 5 + 5 = __10__   4 + 4 = __8__   9 + 9 = __18__

4.
$$\begin{array}{cccccc}
7 & 5 & 2 & 8 & 3 & 6 \\
+\,7 & +\,5 & +\,2 & +\,8 & +\,3 & +\,6 \\
\hline
14 & 10 & 4 & 16 & 6 & 12
\end{array}$$

5.
$$\begin{array}{cccccc}
1 & 4 & 3 & 9 & 5 & 7 \\
+\,1 & +\,4 & +\,3 & +\,9 & +\,5 & +\,7 \\
\hline
2 & 8 & 6 & 18 & 10 & 14
\end{array}$$

▶ Problem Solving

Draw a picture to solve.
Write the addition sentence.

6. Kenny has 6 toy trucks.
Tyler has 6. How many
toy trucks do they have in all?

__6__ + __6__ = __12__
toy trucks

Check children's work.

Harcourt Brace School Publishers

More Doubles

▶ **Vocabulary**

Circle the **doubles-plus-one** fact ▮ red ▯.

Circle the **doubles-minus-one** fact ▮ blue ▯.

$4 + 4 = 8$ blue $\left(\ 4 + 3 = 7\ \right)$ red $\left(\ 4 + 5 = 9\ \right)$

Complete the addition table.
Color each doubles sum green.
Color each doubles-plus-one sum yellow.
Color each doubles-minus-one sum purple.

+	0	1	2	3	4	5	6	7	8	9
0	0 green	1 yellow	2	3	4	5	6	7	8	9
1	1 purple	2 green	3 yellow	4	5	6	7	8	9	10
2	2	3 purple	4 green	5 yellow	6	7	8	9	10	11
3	3	4	5 purple	6 green	7 yellow	8	9	10	11	12
4	4	5	6	7 purple	8 green	9 yellow	10	11	12	13
5	5	6	7	8	9 purple	10 green	11 yellow	12	13	14
6	6	7	8	9	10	11 purple	12 green	13 yellow	14	15
7	7	8	9	10	11	12	13 purple	14 green	15 yellow	16
8	8	9	10	11	12	13	14	15 purple	16 green	17 yellow
9	9	10	11	12	13	14	15	16	17 purple	18 green

Name _____

Adding on a Ten-Frame

Use a ten-frame and counters.
Write the sum.

1.

$$9 + 6 = 15$$ $$10 + 5 = 15$$ $$10 + 5 = 15$$

2.

$$7 + 9 = 16$$ $$3 + 9 = 12$$ $$9 + 2 = 11$$ $$9 + 8 = 17$$ $$8 + 9 = 17$$

3.

$$9 + 3 = 12$$ $$1 + 9 = 10$$ $$9 + 4 = 13$$ $$9 + 7 = 16$$ $$9 + 5 = 14$$

4.

$$2 + 9 = 11$$ $$6 + 9 = 15$$ $$5 + 9 = 14$$ $$1 + 9 = 10$$ $$4 + 9 = 13$$

▶ **Problem Solving**

Write the addition sentence. Solve.

5. Martin has 3 flowers. He picks 9 more. How many flowers does Martin have in all?

___3___ + ___9___ = ___12___ flowers

6. Ann has 9 flowers. She picks 2 more. How many flowers does she have in all?

___9___ + ___2___ = ___11___ flowers

Harcourt Brace School Publishers

Make a Ten

Use a ten-frame and counters.
Find the sum.

1.
$$7 + 5 = 12$$ $$6 + 7 = 13$$ $$8 + 6 = 14$$ $$9 + 1 = 10$$ $$3 + 8 = 11$$ $$5 + 7 = 12$$

2.
$$7 + 4 = 11$$ $$6 + 8 = 14$$ $$9 + 6 = 15$$ $$7 + 6 = 13$$ $$7 + 7 = 14$$ $$6 + 9 = 15$$

3.
$$7 + 5 = 12$$ $$5 + 8 = 13$$ $$8 + 4 = 12$$ $$9 + 2 = 11$$ $$7 + 8 = 15$$ $$3 + 7 = 10$$

4.
$$8 + 2 = 10$$ $$8 + 8 = 16$$ $$8 + 5 = 13$$ $$8 + 3 = 11$$ $$9 + 9 = 18$$ $$7 + 9 = 16$$

▶ **Problem Solving**

Write the addition sentence. Solve.

5. Ana's dad bought 4 bunches of red grapes and 7 bunches of green grapes. How many bunches of grapes did he buy in all?

__4__ + __7__ = __11__
bunches

6. Jon's mom bought 9 green apples and 8 red ones. How many apples did she buy in all?

__9__ + __8__ = __17__
apples

Adding Three Addends

Write the sum.

1.
```
   6        6        3        4
   2        6        1        7
 + 9      + 4      + 8      + 2
  17       16       12       13
```

2.
```
   3        5        7        4
   1        8        5        3
 + 3      + 2      + 5      + 4
   7       15       17       11
```

3.
```
   8        7        4        2
   2        6        1        6
 + 9      + 4      + 4      + 2
  19       17        9       10
```

4.
```
   3        9        2        9
   4        0        4        5
 + 1      + 9      + 6      + 2
   8       18       12       16
```

Check children's work.

▶ **Problem Solving**

Draw a picture to solve.

5. Renee has 5 red pens, 3 yellow pens, and 3 green pens. How many pens does she have in all?

_____11_____ pens

Relating Addition and Subtraction

Add or subtract.

1.
$$9 + 7 = 16$$
$$16 - 7 = 9$$
$$7 + 6 = 13$$
$$13 - 6 = 7$$
$$5 + 6 = 11$$
$$11 - 6 = 5$$

2.
$$8 + 7 = 15$$
$$15 - 7 = 8$$
$$9 + 8 = 17$$
$$17 - 8 = 9$$
$$7 + 5 = 12$$
$$12 - 5 = 7$$

3.
$$8 + 2 = \underline{10}$$
$$10 - 2 = \underline{8}$$

4.
$$4 + 3 = \underline{7}$$
$$7 - 3 = \underline{4}$$

5.
$$7 + 7 = \underline{14}$$
$$14 - 7 = \underline{7}$$

6.
$$3 + 8 = \underline{11}$$
$$11 - 8 = \underline{3}$$

7.
$$9 + 4 = \underline{13}$$
$$13 - 4 = \underline{9}$$

8.
$$8 + 9 = \underline{17}$$
$$17 - 9 = \underline{8}$$

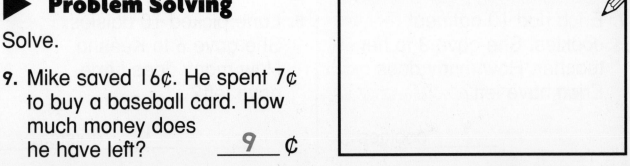

▶ **Problem Solving**

Solve.

9. Mike saved 16¢. He spent 7¢ to buy a baseball card. How much money does he have left? ___9___ ¢

Subtracting on a Number Line

Subtract. Use the number line.

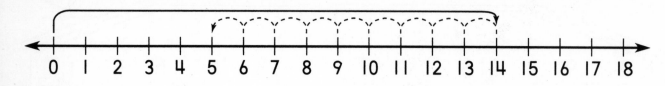

0 1 2 3 4 5 6 7 8 9 10 11 12 13 14 15 16 17 18

1. 14 − 9 = __5__   13 − 6 = __7__   15 − 8 = __7__

2. 17 − 8 = __9__   12 − 9 = __3__   16 − 9 = __7__

3. 16 − 8 = __8__   11 − 4 = __7__   12 − 8 = __4__

4. 13 − 7 = __6__   12 − 5 = __7__   17 − 9 = __8__

5. 12 − 6 = __6__   11 − 7 = __4__   10 − 4 = __6__

6. 14 − 5 = __9__   10 − 8 = __2__   12 − 3 = __9__

▶ Problem Solving

Solve. Use the number line.

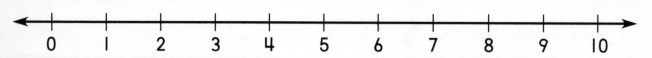

0 1 2 3 4 5 6 7 8 9 10

7. Erica had 10 oatmeal cookies. She gave 3 to her teacher. How many does Erica have left?

__7__ cookies

8. Lane picked 10 daisies. She gave 6 to Keesha. How many does Lane have left?

__4__ daisies

Harcourt Brace School Publishers

Name _____

Fact Families

Write the fact family for the set of numbers.

1.

11, 4, 7

$$4 + 7 = 11 \quad 11 - 4 = 7 \quad 7 + 4 = 11 \quad 11 - 7 = 4$$

2.

14, 6, 8

$$6 + 8 = 14 \quad 14 - 6 = 8 \quad 8 + 6 = 14 \quad 14 - 8 = 6$$

3.

16, 9, 7

$$7 + 9 = 16 \quad 16 - 7 = 9 \quad 9 + 7 = 16 \quad 16 - 9 = 7$$

4.
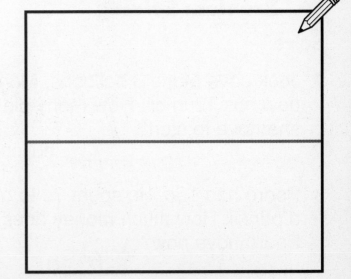

13, 9, 4

$$4 + 9 = 13 \quad 13 - 4 = 9 \quad 9 + 4 = 13 \quad 13 - 9 = 4$$

▶ **Problem Solving**

Solve.

5. Bill had 4 fish. He caught 8 more. How many fish does he have in all? __12__ fish

6. Juan had 8 balloons. He gave 3 to Lei. How many balloons does Juan have left? __5__ balloon

Missing Addends

Draw more fish. Write the missing addend to complete the number sentence.

1.

$$\begin{array}{r} 8 \\ +\ 7 \\ \hline 15 \end{array}$$

2.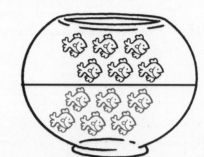

$$\begin{array}{r} 6 \\ +\ 6 \\ \hline 12 \end{array}$$

3.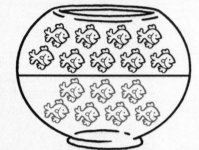

$$\begin{array}{r} 9 \\ +\ 7 \\ \hline 16 \end{array}$$

4.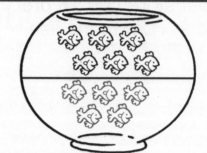

$$\begin{array}{r} 7 \\ +\ 7 \\ \hline 14 \end{array}$$

5.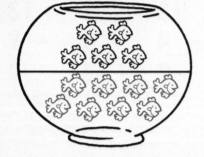

$$\begin{array}{r} 5 \\ +\ 8 \\ \hline 13 \end{array}$$

6.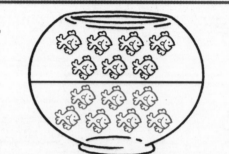

$$\begin{array}{r} 6 \\ +\ 5 \\ \hline 11 \end{array}$$

▶ **Problem Solving**

Solve.

7. Jack gave Marie 3 balloons. Marie now has 12 in all. How many did she have to start?

___9___ balloons

8. Pedro had 15¢. He spent 9¢ to buy a pencil. How much money does Pedro have now?

___6___ ¢

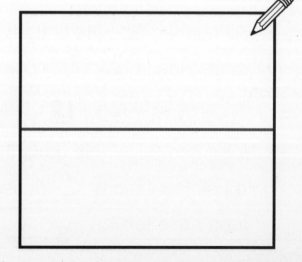

Problem Solving • Choose the Operation

Write **+** or **−**. Then solve.

1. At the zoo, 9 bears and 7 cubs jumped into the water. How many in all were in the water?

   9 ⊕ 7 = __16__

   __16__ bears

2. There were 7 cats and 8 kittens on the porch. How many were on the porch?

   8 ⊕ 7 = __15__

   __15__ cats

3. The pet store had 16 pretty fish. It sold 9. How many fish were left?

   16 ⊖ 9 = __7__

   __7__ fish

4. There were 9 pears in a basket. John ate 3. How many were left?

   9 ⊖ 3 = __6__

   __6__ pears

5. There were 7 children in the yard and 3 children in the house. How many children were there in all?

   7 ⊕ 3 = __10__

   __10__ children

Grouping Tens

 **Vocabulary**

Circle the picture that shows 1 ten.

1.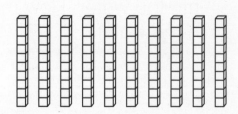

_____

Circle groups of tens.
Write how many tens and ones.

2.

_____1_____ ten = _____10_____ ones

3.

_____2_____ tens = _____20_____ ones

4.

_____5_____ tens = _____50_____ ones

 Problem Solving

Write how many tens.

5.  30 = ___3___ tens

6. 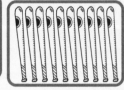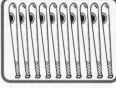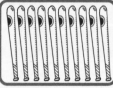 80 = ___8___ tens

Harcourt Brace School Publishers

Tens and Ones to 50

Write the number.

1.

3 tens 4 ones = __34__

2.

4 tens 6 ones = __46__

3.

1 ten 3 ones = __13__

4.

5 tens 0 ones = __50__

5.

2 tens 1 one = __21__

6.

0 tens 8 ones = __8__

7.

1 ten 2 ones = __12__

8.

2 tens 5 ones = __25__

9.

3 tens 7 ones = __37__

10.

4 tens 9 ones = __49__

▶ Problem Solving

Solve.

11. Jeni went outside to collect leaves.
She put her leaves into 7 groups of
ten. How many leaves does she have?

__70__ leaves

12. Latisha went to the beach to gather
shells. She put her shells into
2 groups of ten and had 5 left over.
How many shells does she have?

__25__ shells

Tens and Ones to 100

Write how many tens and ones.
Then write the number.

1.

___6___ tens ___2___ ones = ___62___

2.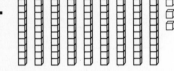

___9___ tens ___3___ ones = ___93___

3.

___5___ tens ___8___ ones = ___58___

4.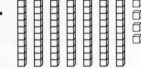

___7___ tens ___4___ ones = ___74___

5.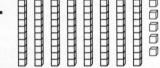

___8___ tens ___5___ ones = ___85___

6.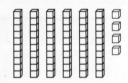

___6___ tens ___4___ ones = ___64___

▶ **Problem Solving**

Which group is easier to count? Circle it. Tell why.

7.

Use a Model

Look at the model.
Circle the number that it shows.

1.

   $\big($12$\big)$ 21   31

2.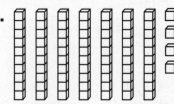

   $\big($74$\big)$ 47   41

3.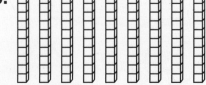

   85   51 $\big($35$\big)$

4.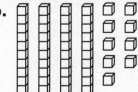

   22    $\big($82$\big)$ 32

5.

   $\big($90$\big)$ 9   91

6.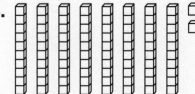

   94   45 $\big($49$\big)$

▶ **Problem Solving**

Write the mystery number.

7. Jerry's mystery number
   has a 7 in the tens place and
   a 4 in the ones place.

   His mystery
   number is __74__ .

8. Emma's mystery number has
   a 9 in the tens place and a
   3 in the ones place.

   Her mystery
   number is __93__ .

Exploring Estimation

Look at each group of beans.
Use these groups to help you choose the better estimate.

10 beans

25 beans

50 beans

1.

(about 10 beans)
about 25 beans

2.

about 25 beans
(about 50 beans)

3.

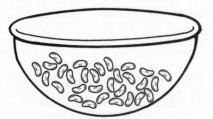

about 10 beans
(about 25 beans)

4.

(about 10 beans)
about 25 beans

▶ Problem Solving

Circle the better estimate.

5.

more than 30
(fewer than 30)

6.

more than 20
fewer than 20

Harcourt Brace School Publishers

Skip-Counting by Fives and Tens

Write the missing numbers.
Count by fives. Color those boxes yellow.
Count by tens. Circle those numbers.

1	2	3	4	5	6	7	8	9	⑩
11	12	13	14	15	16	17	18	19	⑳
21	22	23	24	25	26	27	28	29	㉚
31	32	33	34	35	36	37	38	39	㊵
41	42	43	44	45	46	47	48	49	㊿
51	52	53	54	55	56	57	58	59	60
61	62	63	64	65	66	67	68	69	70
71	72	73	74	75	76	77	78	79	80
81	82	83	84	85	86	87	88	89	90
91	92	93	94	95	96	97	98	99	100

▶ Problem Solving

Write the answer.

1. Matt puts his toy cars in groups
   of ten. He has 3 groups and
   7 left over. How many cars does
   Matt have?

   ___37___ cars

Skip-Counting by Twos and Threes

Count by twos. Color those boxes red.
Count by threes. Circle those numbers.

Check children's coloring.

red	red	red	red	red

1	2	(3)	4	5	(6)	7	8	(9)	10
11	(12)	13	14	(15)	16	17	(18)	19	20
(21)	22	23	(24)	25	26	(27)	28	29	(30)
31	32	(33)	34	35	(36)	37	38	(39)	40
41	(42)	43	44	(45)	46	47	(48)	49	50
(51)	52	53	(54)	55	56	(57)	58	59	(60)
61	62	(63)	64	65	(66)	67	68	(69)	70
71	(72)	73	74	(75)	76	77	(78)	79	80
(81)	82	83	(84)	85	86	(87)	88	89	(90)
91	92	(93)	94	95	(96)	97	98	(99)	100

▶ **Problem Solving**

Continue the pattern.

1. 7, 9, 11, __13__, __15__, __17__, __19__

2. 5, 10, 15, __20__, __25__, __30__, __35__

3. 3, 6, 9, __12__, __15__, __18__, __21__

Harcourt Brace School Publishers

Even and Odd Numbers

Draw the number of cubes.
Write **even** or **odd.**

1.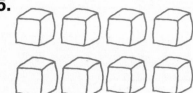

13   <u>odd</u>

2.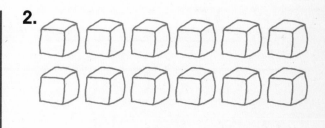

12   <u>even</u>

3.

7   <u>odd</u>

4.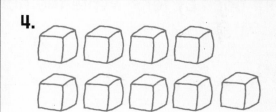

9   <u>odd</u>

5.

8   <u>even</u>

6.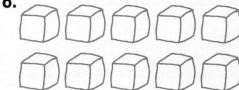

10   <u>even</u>

▶ **Problem Solving**

Write the sum.
Then circle even sums.

7. 6 + 6 = (12)

8. 9 + 8 = 17

9. 4 + 5 = 9

10. 5 + 5 = (10)

Counting On and Back by Tens

Count on by tens. Write the number.

1.

35, __45__ , __55__ , __65__ , 75, __85__ , __95__

2.

16, 26, __36__ , __46__ , __56__ , __66__ , __76__ , __86__ , __96__

Count back by tens. Write the number.

3.

60, __50__ , __40__ , __30__ , __20__ , __10__ , 0

4.

83, __73__ , __63__ , __53__ , 43, __33__ , __23__ , __13__

5.

72, __62__ , __52__ , __42__ , 32, __22__ , __12__ , __2__

▶ **Problem Solving**

Solve.

6. David has 51 pine cones.
He got 10 more. How many
pine cones does he
have in all?

___61___ pine cones

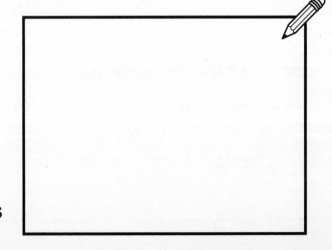

Problem Solving • Look for a Pattern

Write the missing numbers. Write the rule.

1.

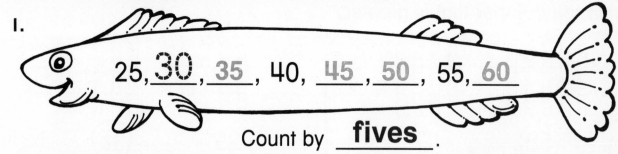

25, _30_, _35_, 40, _45_, _50_, 55, _60_

Count by ____**fives**____.

2.

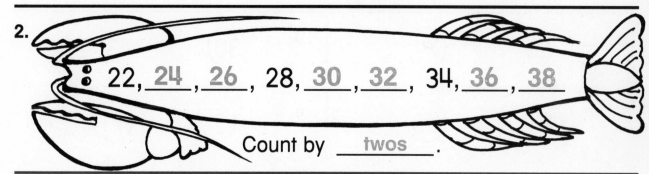

22, _24_, _26_, 28, _30_, _32_, 34, _36_, _38_

Count by ____twos____.

3.

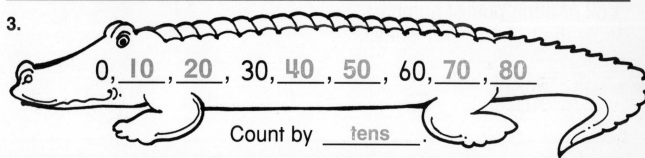

0, _10_, _20_, 30, _40_, _50_, 60, _70_, _80_

Count by ____tens____.

4.

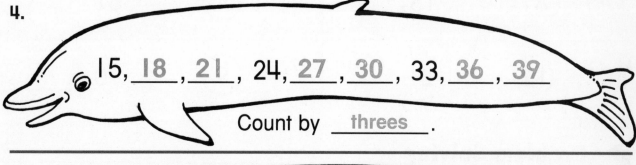

15, _18_, _21_, 24, _27_, _30_, 33, _36_, _39_

Count by ____threes____.

5.

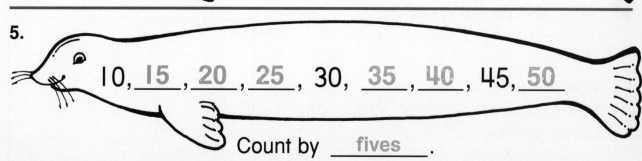

10, _15_, _20_, _25_, 30, _35_, _40_, 45, _50_

Count by ____fives____.

Harcourt Brace School Publishers

Comparing Numbers

Look at each pair of numbers.
Circle the number that is greater.

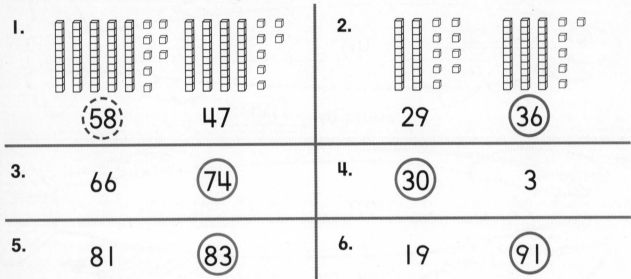

1. (58)   47   2.   29   (36)

---

3.   66   (74)   4. (30)   3

---

5.   81   (83)   6.   19   (91)

Look at each pair of numbers.
Circle the number that is less.

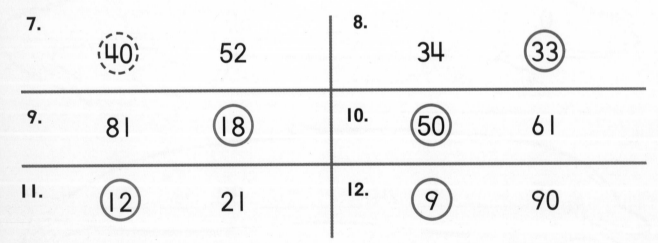

7. (40)   52   8.   34   (33)

---

9.   81   (18)   10. (50)   61

---

11. (12)   21   12. (9)   90

▶ **Problem Solving**

Solve.

13. Josh has 48 baseball cards, and Bill
    has 51 baseball cards. Who has
    more cards?

    ___Bill___

Greater Than and Less Than

Write greater or less.
Then write < or > in the circle.

1. 74 is ___less___ than 89.

74 (<) 89

2. 98 is ___greater___ than 87.

98 (>) 87

3. 48 is ___greater___ than 43.

48 (>) 43

4. 88 is ___less___ than 99.

88 (<) 99

5. 8 is ___greater___ than 7.

8 (>) 7

6. 24 is ___less___ than 38.

24 (<) 38

7. 19 is ___greater___ than 16.

19 (>) 16

8. 55 is ___greater___ than 50.

55 (>) 50

▶ **Problem Solving**

Write < or > in the circle.
Then answer the question.

9. Todd caught 9 fish. Abdul caught 12 fish. Who caught more?

9 (<) 12

Abdul
_____

Ordering Numbers: After, Before, Between

Write the number that is just after,
just before, or between.

1.
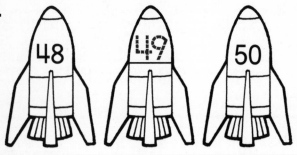

2.

3.

4.

5.
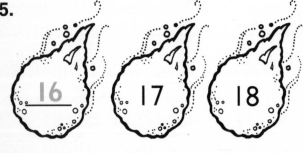

6.

▶ **Problem Solving**

Write the answer.

7. Joan had 9 stickers. She decided to
buy a new sticker every week. The
next week she had 10 stickers.
The following week she had 11
stickers. How many stickers did she
have the week after that?

9, 10, 11, ___12___ stickers

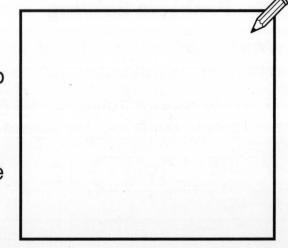

Harcourt Brace School Publishers

Ordinal Numbers

▶ Vocabulary

Circle the ordinal numbers.   (sixteenth)   16   (16th)

Follow the chart. Color the boxes.

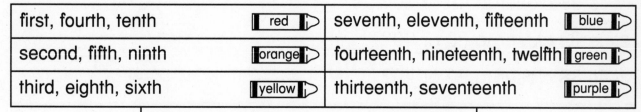

first, fourth, tenth	red ▷	seventh, eleventh, fifteenth	blue ▷
second, fifth, ninth	orange ▷	fourteenth, nineteenth, twelfth	green ▷
third, eighth, sixth	yellow ▷	thirteenth, seventeenth	purple ▷

sixteenth, eighteenth, twentieth black ▷

twentieth	black
nineteenth	green
eighteenth	black
seventeenth	purple
sixteenth	black
fifteenth	blue
fourteenth	green
thirteenth	purple
twelfth	green
eleventh	blue
tenth	red
ninth	orange
eighth	yellow
seventh	blue
sixth	yellow
fifth	orange
fourth	red
third	yellow
second	orange
first	red

Using a Number Line to Estimate

Find the number on the number line.
Write the ten the number is closer to.

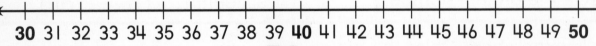

30 31 32 33 34 35 36 37 38 39 **40** 41 42 43 44 45 46 47 48 49 **50**

1. Is 49 closer to 40 or 50? __50__

2. Is 33 closer to 30 or 40? __30__

3. Is 38 closer to 30 or 40? __40__

50 51 52 53 54 55 56 57 58 59 **60** 61 62 63 64 65 66 67 68 69 **70**

4. Is 51 closer to 50 or 60? __50__

5. Is 67 closer to 60 or 70? __70__

6. Is 64 closer to 60 or 70? __60__

70 71 72 73 74 75 76 77 78 79 **80** 81 82 83 84 85 86 87 88 89 **90**

7. Is 82 closer to 80 or 90? __80__

8. Is 76 closer to 70 or 80? __80__

9. Is 73 closer to 70 or 80? __70__

▶ **Problem Solving**

Solve.

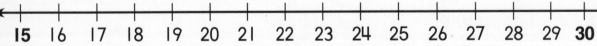

15 16 17 18 19 20 21 22 23 24 25 26 27 28 29 **30**

10. Carmen wants to buy a new radio.
One costs 20 dollars and the other
costs 30 dollars. Carmen has saved
23 dollars. Circle the radio she is
closer to buying.

Harcourt Brace School Publishers

Name _____

 LESSON
6.1

Pennies, Nickels, and Dimes

▶ **Vocabulary**

Write the value.

1.

I penny = ___I___ ¢   I nickel = ___5___ ¢   I dime = __10__ ¢

Count on to find the total amount.

2.

__10__ ¢, __20__ ¢, __30__ ¢, __35__ ¢, __40__ ¢, __41__ ¢ | 41 | ¢

3.

__10__ ¢, __15__ ¢, __20__ ¢, __25__ ¢, __30__ ¢, __31__ ¢ | 31 | ¢

4.

__10__ ¢, __20__ ¢, __30__ ¢, __40__ ¢, __50__ ¢, __51__ ¢ | 51 | ¢

▶ **Problem Solving**

Write the amount.

5. Carrie has 2 dimes, 2 nickels, and 2 pennies. How much money does she have?

__32__ ¢

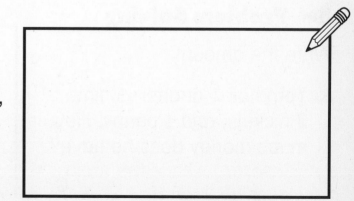

Harcourt Brace School Publishers

Nickels, Dimes, and Quarters

► **Vocabulary**

Write the value.

I.

I nickel = __5__ ¢   I dime = __10__ ¢   I quarter = __25__ ¢

Count on to find the total amount.

2.

__25__ ¢, __35__ ¢, __45__ ¢, __55__ ¢, __60__ ¢, __61__ ¢   [61] ¢

3.

__25__ ¢, __35__ ¢, __45__ ¢, __46__ ¢, __47__ ¢, __48__ ¢   [48] ¢

4.

__10__ ¢, __20__ ¢, __30__ ¢, __31__ ¢, __32__ ¢   [32] ¢

► **Problem Solving**

Write the amount.

5. Tom has I quarter, I dime, 2 nickels, and I penny. How much money does he have?

__46__ ¢

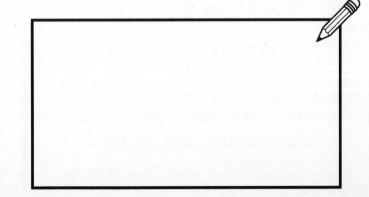

Harcourt Brace School Publishers

Counting Collections

Draw and label the coins in order from
greatest to least value. Find the total amount.

1.

25¢   10¢   10¢   5¢   **50** ¢

2.

25¢   5¢   5¢   5¢   1¢   **41** ¢

3.

25¢   5¢   1¢   1¢   1¢   **33** ¢

▶ **Problem Solving**

Write the amount.

4. Keesha found 3 pennies, 2
   nickels, 1 quarter, and 1 dime.
   How much money did she find?

   48 ¢

Counting Half-Dollars

Write the total amount.

1.

62 ¢

2.

89 ¢

3.

56 ¢

4.

98 ¢

▶ **Problem Solving**

Write the amount.

5. Jamal has 1 half-dollar, 4 dimes, and 3 pennies. How much money does he have?

93 ¢

6. Cody has saved 1 half-dollar, 2 dimes, 1 nickel, and 4 pennies. How much money has he saved?

79 ¢

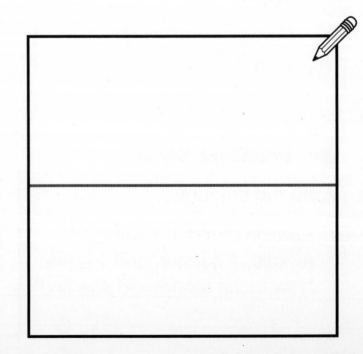

▶ Problem Solving • Act It Out

Use coins to show the price.
Write how many of each coin you used.

I.

46¢ ANIMAL CARDS

0 __ 1 __ 1 __ 2 __ 1 __

---

2. 70¢  **Answers will vary.**

___ ___ ___ ___ ___

---

3. 99¢  **Answers will vary.**

___ ___ ___ ___ ___

---

4.  38¢ MARKERS **Answers will vary.**

___ ___ ___ ___ ___

---

5.  55¢ **Answers will vary.**

___ ___ ___ ___ ___

Combinations of Coins

Use coins. Show the amount of
money in two ways. Draw and label
the coins you use.

Answers will vary.

1.

65¢

(10¢) (10¢)

(25¢)

(10¢) (10¢)

2.

47¢

3.

89¢

▶ **Problem Solving**

Draw the coins. Write the amount.

4. Anthony has 25¢.
His mother gives him 25¢
more. How much money does
he have?

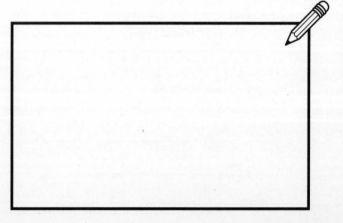

__50__ ¢

Equal Amounts Using Fewest Coins

Write the amount. Then show the same
amount with fewer coins. Draw and label
the coins you use.

1.

<u>65</u> ¢

2.

<u>90</u> ¢

3.

<u>75</u> ¢

Name_____

Comparing Amounts to Prices

Write the amount.
Write the names and prices
of the two foods you could buy.

Ice Cream
58¢

Peanut Butter
97¢

Bread
95¢

Cheese
83¢

Fruit Bar
65¢

Banana
79¢

80 ¢

85 ¢

97 ¢

Answers will vary.

1. _____ _____ ¢

2. _____ _____ ¢

3. _____ _____ ¢

4. _____ _____ ¢

5. _____ _____ ¢

6. _____ _____ ¢

▶ **Problem Solving**

Write the answer.

7. Jamie has 65¢. She wants to buy
   a book. The red book costs 59¢.
   The green book costs 72¢. Which
   book can she buy?

   the red book

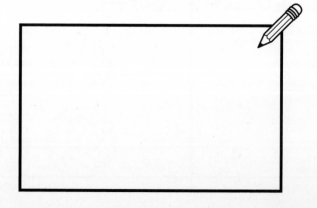

Harcourt Brace School Publishers

Making Change

Count on from the price to find the change.

1. You have 55¢.

You buy a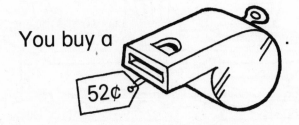

___53___ ¢, ___54___ ¢, ___55___ ¢

Your change is ___3___ ¢.

2. You have 49¢.

You buy a

___48___ ¢, ___49___ ¢

Your change is ___2___ ¢.

3. You have 74¢.

You buy a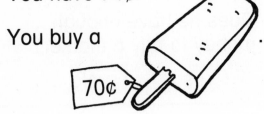

___71___ ¢, ___72___ ¢, ___73___ ¢, ___74___ ¢

Your change is ___4___ ¢.

▶ **Problem Solving**

Use coins to solve.

4. Alexa has 50¢. She buys a book for 47¢. How much change does she get?

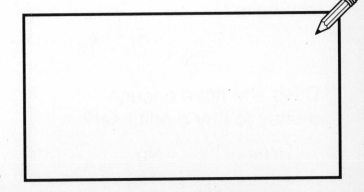

Alexa gets ___3___ ¢ change.

Problem Solving • Act It Out

Use coins to solve.
Then circle **Yes** or **No**.

1. Brittany has 1 quarter,
2 dimes, and 3 nickels.
How much money does
she have?

   _____60_____ ¢

   Does she have enough
   money to buy scissors?

   Yes   (No)

2. Jon has 1 half-dollar,
1 quarter, and 1 dime.
How much money does
he have?

   _____85_____ ¢

   Does he have enough
   money to buy a paintbrush?

   Yes   (No)

3. Edmond has 1 quarter,
2 dimes, 3 nickels, and
2 pennies. How much
money does he have?

   _____62_____ ¢

   Does he have enough
   money to buy a marker?

   (Yes)   No

4. Ming has 1 quarter,
2 nickels, and 3 pennies.
How much money does
she have?

   _____38_____ ¢

   Does she have enough
   money to buy a paint set?

   (Yes)   No

5. Ben has 1 half-dollar,
1 quarter, 1 dime, 1 nickel,
and 2 pennies. How much
money does he have?

   _____92_____ ¢

   Does he have enough
   money to buy paper?

   Yes   (No)

Harcourt Brace School Publishers

Hour and Half-Hour

▶ Vocabulary

Use the words to name the clock hands.

1. minute hand
   hour hand

_____   _____

- - - - - - - - - - - - -   - - - - - - - - - - - - -

__hour hand__   __minute hand__

Read the time. Then write the time.

2.

5:30   **7:00**   **1:30**   **10:30**

3.

2:00   **7:30**   **4:00**   **3:30**

4.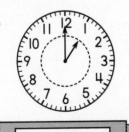

1:00   **9:00**   **8:30**   **6:00**

Telling Time to 5 Minutes

Write the time.

1.

2:00

2:05

2:10

2.

2:15

2:20

2:25

3.

2:30

2:35

2:40

 Problem Solving

Write the time. Draw the hands to show the time.

4. Hailey leaves school at 3:25. She gets to her piano lesson 5 minutes later. What time does she get to her lesson?

3:30

Harcourt Brace School Publishers

Name _____

Telling Time to 15 Minutes

Write the time.

1.

2:45 10:30 5:15

2.

9:30 6:45 1:30

3.

3:45 11:15 4:15

▶ **Problem Solving**

Use the clocks. Write the answer.

4. Billy walked to Rosa's house. He left home at

He got to Rosa's house at

How long did Billy walk?

 .  .

15 ___ minutes

Practice Telling Time

Draw the minute hand to show the time.

1.

10:15

7:45

2:30

2.

4:45

1:15

9:30

Write the time.

3.

3:25

8:10

11:20

4.

5:40

10:05

6:35

▶ Problem Solving

Write the time. Draw the hands to show the time.

5. Joey got to the zoo at 2:00. He saw the lions fifteen minutes later. What time did Joey see the lions?

2:15

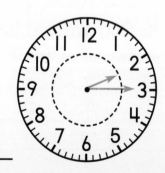

Elapsed Time

Read the clock. Use the clock to solve the problem.
Write the new time.

1. Jerome goes to Stephanie's house at  . He leaves Stephanie's house 2 hours later. What time does he leave?

   12:00

2. The dance show starts at  . The show ends 3 hours later. What time does it end?

   4:30

3. Sasha starts cleaning her room at  . She cleans for 30 minutes. What time does she finish cleaning?

   2:45

4. Sue Ling goes shopping with her mom at  . She and her mom get home 2 hours later. What time do they get home?

   8:00

▶ **Problem Solving**

Circle the correct answer.

5. Which clock shows 30 minutes after 7 o'clock?

Name _____

Reading a Calendar

Fill in the calendar for this month.
Then use the calendar to answer the questions.

Month will vary.						
Sunday	**Monday**	**Tuesday**	**Wednesday**	**Thursday**	**Friday**	**Saturday**

1. On which day does the
   month begin? _____ **Answer will vary.**

2. What is the date of the third
   Monday in the month? _____ **Answer will vary.**

3. How many days are in
   the month? _____ **Answer will vary.**

4. On which day will the
   next month start? _____ **Answer will vary.**

▶ **Problem Solving**

5. Kate's soccer team has practice every   **Answer will vary.**
   Tuesday and Friday night. How many
   practices does she have this month?   _____ practices

Name _____

Using a Calendar

Use the calendar to answer the questions.

 January

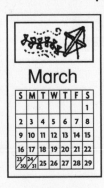 February

 March

 April

 May

 June

 July

 August

 September

 October

 November

 December

1. Which is the twelfth month in the year?

December

2. What is the second month of the year?

February

3. How many Tuesdays are there in April?

five

4. What day is one week before September 12?

September 5

5. Name one month that has 31 days.

Answers will vary.

6. How many days are there in February?

28

▶ **Problem Solving**

7. What will be the day and date two weeks from today?

Answers will vary.

Early or Late

Write each time. Then write **early** or **late.**

1. The school play starts at `11:15`.

   11:15

   Sam gets there at `11:20`.

   11:20

   Is Sam early or late?

   late

2. The city library opens at .

   9:00

   Karen gets there at .

   8:45

   Is Karen early or late?

   early

3. The class party starts at `3:00`.

   3:00

   Jamal gets there at `2:55`.

   2:55

   Is Jamal early or late?

   early

4. The baseball game starts at 🕐.

   1:00

   Misha gets there at 🕐.

   1:10

   Is Misha early or late?

   late

▶ **Problem Solving**

5. Circle the person who came into the room first.

Harcourt Brace School Publishers

Sequencing Events

Carol and her dad go to the store. Number the events
in order. Use the clocks to write the time of each event.

3   4:25

1   4:00

2   4:20

4   4:35

▶ **Problem Solving**

Use the clocks. Write the answer.

How many minutes did it take Kevin to paint his picture? __20__ minutes

Problem Solving • Reading a Schedule

Use the schedule to answer the questions.

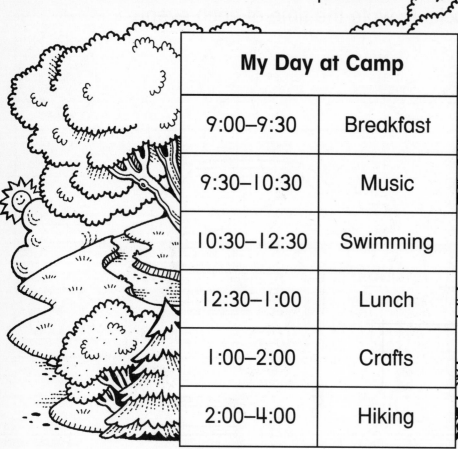

My Day at Camp	
9:00–9:30	Breakfast
9:30–10:30	Music
10:30–12:30	Swimming
12:30–1:00	Lunch
1:00–2:00	Crafts
2:00–4:00	Hiking

1. What time does breakfast begin?

    9:00

2. What time does lunch end?

    1:00

3. How long is hiking?

    2 hours

4. How long is lunch?

    30 minutes

5. How long is breakfast?

    30 minutes

6. How much time passes from the end of lunch to the end of crafts?

    1 hour

Harcourt Brace School Publishers

Regrouping Ones as Tens

Use Workmat 3 and base-ten blocks. Add.

Join the ones. Write how many.	Can you make a ten?	If so, regroup 10 ones as a ten. Write how many tens and ones.
1. $8 + 7 = \underline{15}$ ones	(Yes) No	$\underline{1}$ ten $\underline{5}$ ones
2. $4 + 6 = \underline{10}$ ones	(Yes) No	$\underline{1}$ ten $\underline{0}$ ones
3. $9 + 2 = \underline{11}$ ones	(Yes) No	$\underline{1}$ ten $\underline{1}$ one
4. $5 + 4 = \underline{9}$ ones	Yes (No)	$\underline{0}$ ten $\underline{9}$ ones
5. $7 + 7 = \underline{14}$ ones	(Yes) No	$\underline{1}$ ten $\underline{4}$ ones
6. $8 + 9 = \underline{17}$ ones	(Yes) No	$\underline{1}$ ten $\underline{7}$ ones

▶ **Problem Solving**

Check children's work.

7. Eddie has 7 marbles. Karim has 6 marbles. How many do they have in all?

$\underline{13}$ marbles

8. If Eddie and Karim put the marbles in groups of ten, how many tens will they have?

$\underline{1}$ ten

Modeling One-Digit and Two-Digit Addition

Use Workmat 3 and base-ten blocks. Add.

	Show.	Can you make a ten? If so, regroup 10 ones as 1 ten.	Write how many in all.
1.	8 + 14	(Yes) No	22
2.	14 + 5	Yes (No)	19
3.	9 + 15	(Yes) No	24
4.	12 + 8	(Yes) No	20
5.	15 + 7	(Yes) No	22
6.	11 + 7	Yes (No)	18
7.	6 + 18	(Yes) No	24
8.	6 + 7	(Yes) No	13

▶ **Problem Solving**

Check children's work.

9. Joe has 12 stickers. Maria has 9 stickers. How many do they have in all?

_____21_____ stickers

How many tens? ___2___ tens

How many ones? ___1___ one

Harcourt Brace School Publishers

Modeling Two-Digit Addition

Work with a partner. Use Workmat 3 and
base-ten blocks. Add.

Show.	Can you make a ten? If so, regroup 10 ones as 1 ten.		Write how many in all.
1. 18 + 14	(Yes)	No	32
2. 15 + 12	Yes	(No)	27
3. 19 + 11	(Yes)	No	30
4. 16 + 19	(Yes)	No	35
5. 11 + 14	Yes	(No)	25
6. 14 + 15	Yes	(No)	29
7. 16 + 17	(Yes)	No	33

▶ **Problem Solving**

Check children's work.

8. Zack has 13 baseball cards.
Marco has 11. How many cards
do the boys have in all?

____24____ baseball cards

How many tens? ___2___ tens

How many ones? ___4___ ones

Harcourt Brace School Publishers

Recording Two-Digit Addition

Use Workmat 3 and base-ten blocks. Add.

1.

tens	ones
3	9
+1	4
5	3

2.

tens	ones
1	0
+2	7
3	7

3.

tens	ones
2	6
+1	4
4	0

4.

tens	ones
3	5
+2	6
6	1

5.

tens	ones
2	4
+2	8
5	2

6.

tens	ones
1	8
+1	7
3	5

7.

tens	ones
1	4
+1	5
2	9

8.

tens	ones
2	8
+1	8
4	6

▶ **Problem Solving**

Check children's work.

9. Mike's team scored 18 points. Alice's team scored 16 points. How many points in all did the two teams score?

_____34_____ points

How many tens? ___3___ tens

How many ones? ___4___ ones

Problem Solving • Make a Model

Use Workmat 3 and base-ten blocks.
Add. Regroup if you need to. Write the sum.

1. The teacher has 15 blue pencils and
14 red pencils. How many blue and
red pencils does the teacher have?

   __29__ pencils

tens	ones
1	5
+ 1	4
2	9

2. One class has 17 students. Another
class has 18. How many students
are in the two classes?

   __35__ students

tens	ones
1	7
+ 1	8
3	5

3. The bookstore sold 10 books on
Wednesday and 23 books on Thursday.
How many books did the store sell?

   __33__ books

tens	ones
1	0
+ 2	3
3	3

4. There are 16 orange sodas and
14 grape sodas in a cooler. How
many sodas are there in all?

   __30__ sodas

tens	ones
1	6
+ 1	4
3	0

5. There are 25 cows and 17 sheep on
Mr. Johnston's farm. How many cows
and sheep does Mr. Johnston have?

   __42__ cows and sheep

tens	ones
2	5
+ 1	7
4	2

Name_____

Adding One-Digit and Two-Digit Numbers

Add. Regroup if you need to.

1.

tens	ones
1	
5	1
+	9
6	0

tens	ones
1	
3	5
+	9
4	4

tens	ones
1	
7	7
+	7
8	4

tens	ones
1	
4	3
+	8
5	1

2.

tens	ones
1	
8	6
+	5
9	1

tens	ones
1	
1	5
+	8
2	3

tens	ones
2	3
+	4
2	7

tens	ones
1	
4	9
+	1
5	0

3.

tens	ones
1	4
+	4
1	8

tens	ones
1	
5	6
+	6
6	2

tens	ones
1	
6	1
+	9
7	0

tens	ones
1	
2	7
+	9
3	6

▶ **Problem Solving**

4. David has 21 toy dinosaurs and Melissa has 19. How many toy dinosaurs do they have in all?

___40___ dinosaurs

Name _____

LESSON
11.2

Adding Two-Digit Numbers

Add. Regroup if you need to.

1.

tens	ones
2	3
+ 4	5
6	8

tens	ones
1	
1	4
+ 3	6
5	0

tens	ones
1	
7	5
+ 1	6
9	1

tens	ones
1	
3	5
+ 2	6
6	1

2.

tens	ones
1	
6	7
+ 1	9
8	6

tens	ones
1	
5	9
+ 1	8
7	7

tens	ones
1	
5	7
+ 2	6
8	3

tens	ones
1	
4	2
+ 1	9
6	1

3.

tens	ones
1	
2	6
+ 2	6
5	2

tens	ones
1	
4	4
+ 1	7
6	1

tens	ones
1	
4	6
+ 2	5
7	1

tens	ones
1	
5	7
+ 3	8
9	5

▶ **Problem Solving**

Use the pictures to solve.

4. Glen bought a banana and a pear. How much did he spend?

 53 ¢

Harcourt Brace School Publishers

ON MY OWN P65

More About Two-Digit Addition

Add.

1.

$$
\begin{array}{r} {}^{1}53 \\ +\,27 \\ \hline 80 \end{array}
\quad
\begin{array}{r} {}^{1}43 \\ +\,19 \\ \hline 62 \end{array}
\quad
\begin{array}{r} {}^{1}72 \\ +\,26 \\ \hline 98 \end{array}
\quad
\begin{array}{r} {}^{1}35 \\ +\,36 \\ \hline 71 \end{array}
\quad
\begin{array}{r} {}^{1}65 \\ +\,17 \\ \hline 82 \end{array}
\quad
\begin{array}{r} {}^{1}18 \\ +\,15 \\ \hline 33 \end{array}
$$

2.

$$
\begin{array}{r} {}^{1}28 \\ +\,32 \\ \hline 60 \end{array}
\quad
\begin{array}{r} {}^{1}14 \\ +\,27 \\ \hline 41 \end{array}
\quad
\begin{array}{r} {}^{1}36 \\ +\,45 \\ \hline 81 \end{array}
\quad
\begin{array}{r} {}^{1}28 \\ +\,27 \\ \hline 55 \end{array}
\quad
\begin{array}{r} 61 \\ +\,35 \\ \hline 96 \end{array}
\quad
\begin{array}{r} 55 \\ +\,40 \\ \hline 95 \end{array}
$$

3.

$$
\begin{array}{r} 18 \\ +\,20 \\ \hline 38 \end{array}
\quad
\begin{array}{r} {}^{1}25 \\ +\,15 \\ \hline 40 \end{array}
\quad
\begin{array}{r} {}^{1}47 \\ +\,17 \\ \hline 64 \end{array}
\quad
\begin{array}{r} 56 \\ +\,22 \\ \hline 78 \end{array}
\quad
\begin{array}{r} 26 \\ +\,62 \\ \hline 88 \end{array}
\quad
\begin{array}{r} 35 \\ +\,14 \\ \hline 49 \end{array}
$$

4.

$$
\begin{array}{r} 42 \\ +\,53 \\ \hline 95 \end{array}
\quad
\begin{array}{r} {}^{1}17 \\ +\,36 \\ \hline 53 \end{array}
\quad
\begin{array}{r} {}^{1}43 \\ +\,19 \\ \hline 62 \end{array}
\quad
\begin{array}{r} {}^{1}26 \\ +\,46 \\ \hline 72 \end{array}
\quad
\begin{array}{r} 75 \\ +\,14 \\ \hline 89 \end{array}
\quad
\begin{array}{r} 66 \\ +\,33 \\ \hline 99 \end{array}
$$

▶ Problem Solving

5. Marisa saved 38 pennies last month. She saved 41 pennies this month. How many pennies did she save?

   ___79___ pennies

6. At the zoo, Theo saw 26 penguins in the water and 18 penguins on land. How many penguins did Theo see?

   ___44___ penguins

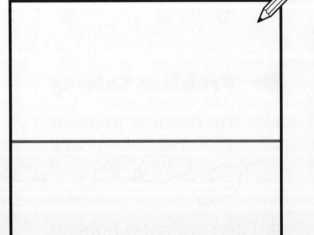

Addition Practice

Add.

1.

25	12	45	49	57	71
+ 18	+ 15	+ 14	+ 12	+ 28	+ 19
43	27	59	61	85	90

2.

22	39	23	16	44	65
+ 10	+ 46	+ 16	+ 46	+ 14	+ 32
32	85	39	62	58	97

▶ Problem Solving

Ms. Jackson's class planted flowers around the school.
Read the chart to find out how many flowers they planted.

	Monday	Tuesday	Wednesday	Thursday	Friday
roses	13	20	15	12	21
pansies	25	14	12	0	0
tulips	0	13	0	13	19
daisies	12	11	18	10	0

Use the chart to answer the questions.

3. How many roses and pansies were planted on Tuesday?   34

4. How many roses and daisies were planted on Wednesday?   33

5. How many flowers were planted on Friday?   40

Problem Solving • Too Much Information

Draw a line through the sentence that is not needed.
Then solve.

1. On Tuesday, 23 birds came to John's feeder. On Wednesday, 48 birds came. ~~16 birds were robins.~~ How many birds came to the feeder?

   __71__ birds

2. Wilbert had 45 marbles. He found 17 more. ~~12 of the marbles had dirt on them.~~ How many marbles in all did Wilbert have?

   __62__ marbles

3. Twila mailed 16 letters on Tuesday. She mailed 20 on Friday. ~~3 letters went to Kansas.~~ How many letters in all did Twila send?

   __36__ letters

4. Pablo saw 36 cars go by his house. Then he saw 24 more. ~~20 of the cars were green.~~ How many cars in all did Pablo see?

   __60__ cars

5. Mrs. Wen's class went to the fair. The students saw 14 rides and 23 animals. ~~13 students bought cotton candy.~~ How many rides and animals in all did Mrs. Wen's class see?

   __37__ rides and animals

Harcourt Brace School Publishers

Regrouping Ten as Ones

Use Workmat 3 and base-ten blocks. Subtract.

Show the tens and ones.	Subtract.	Are there enough ones to subtract? If not, regroup 1 ten as 10 ones.	Write how many tens and ones are left.
1. 3 tens 7 ones	9 ones	Yes (No)	_2_ tens _8_ ones
2. 1 ten 6 ones	6 ones	(Yes) No	_1_ ten _0_ ones
3. 2 tens 5 ones	9 ones	Yes (No)	_1_ ten _6_ ones
4. 4 tens 0 ones	8 ones	Yes (No)	_3_ tens _2_ ones
5. 3 tens 8 ones	7 ones	(Yes) No	_3_ tens _1_ one
6. 3 tens 5 ones	6 ones	Yes (No)	_2_ tens _9_ ones

▶ **Problem Solving**

Draw the tokens to solve.

7. Anita had 18 game tokens. She spent 9 of them. How many tokens does she have left?

_9_ tokens

Modeling One-Digit and Two-Digit Subtraction

Use Workmat 3 and base-ten blocks.
Subtract.

Subtract.	Do you need to regroup?		Write how many are left.
1. 34 − 8	(Yes)	No	26
2. 27 − 6	Yes	(No)	21
3. 45 − 7	(Yes)	No	38
4. 27 − 9	(Yes)	No	18
5. 29 − 9	Yes	(No)	20
6. 38 − 6	Yes	(No)	32
7. 18 − 9	(Yes)	No	9
8. 25 − 7	(Yes)	No	18

▶ **Problem Solving**

9. Albert had 24 toy cars.
He gave 6 to his best friend.
How many toy cars does
Albert have left?

_18_ toy cars

Recording Subtraction

Use Workmat 3 and base-ten blocks.
Subtract.

1.

tens	ones
3	2
−	8
2	4

tens	ones

tens	ones

tens	ones

2.

tens	ones
3	9
−	7
3	2

tens	ones
5	1
−	6
4	5

tens	ones
2	4
−	8
1	6

tens	ones
1	2
−	9
	3

3.

tens	ones
2	5
−	4
2	1

tens	ones
4	8
−	9
3	9

tens	ones
2	9
−	5
2	4

tens	ones
4	5
−	7
3	8

4.

tens	ones
3	3
−	8
2	5

tens	ones
5	8
−	5
5	3

tens	ones
3	7
−	9
2	8

tens	ones
2	6
−	8
1	8

▶ **Problem Solving**

5. Ricky has 19 baseball caps.
If he gives 8 caps to his
baseball team, how many will
he have left?

___11___ baseball caps

Recording Two-Digit Subtraction

Use Workmat 3 and base-ten blocks.
Subtract.

1.

tens	ones
4	2
− 2	4
1	8

tens	ones

tens	ones

tens	ones

2.

tens	ones
5	0
− 1	9
3	1

tens	ones
4	8
− 2	5
2	3

tens	ones
2	5
− 1	7
	8

tens	ones
3	3
− 1	8
1	5

3.

tens	ones
3	5
− 2	5
1	0

tens	ones
4	4
− 2	8
1	6

tens	ones
1	9
− 1	3
	6

tens	ones
5	6
− 2	8
2	8

4.

tens	ones
4	2
− 3	4
	8

tens	ones
3	7
− 2	2
1	5

tens	ones
5	6
− 3	6
2	0

tens	ones
2	7
− 1	8
	9

▶ **Problem Solving**

Circle the correct answer.

5. Susie has 44 peanuts.
   If she gives away 28, how
   many will she have left?

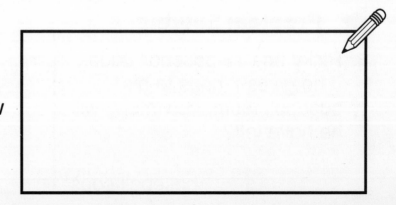

12   (16)   14

Harcourt Brace School Publishers

Problem Solving • Choose the Operation

Use Workmat 3 and base-ten blocks.
Circle **add** or **subtract**.
Write **+** or **−**. Find the sum or difference.

1. Ashlynn has 24 cents. She earns 39 cents.
   How much money does she have in all?

tens	ones
2	4¢
⊕ 3	9¢
6	3¢

   (add)   subtract

2. Steve had 45 bottle caps.
   He gave his sister 25. How many bottle
   caps does he have left?

tens	ones
4	5
⊖ 2	5
2	0

   add   (subtract)

3. At the store, Ana bought 50 stickers
   and 10 pencils. How many items does
   she have in all?

tens	ones
5	0
⊕ 1	0
6	0

   (add)   subtract

4. Ling collected 67 baseball cards.
   Andy collected 23 baseball cards. How
   many more baseball cards does Ling have
   than Andy?

tens	ones
6	7
⊖ 2	3
4	4

   add   (subtract)

5. Marcia found 22 seashells at the beach.
   She gave her mother 9 seashells. How
   many seashells does Marcia have left?

tens	ones
2	2
⊖	9
1	3

   add   (subtract)

Subtracting One-Digit from Two-Digit Numbers

Use Workmat 3 and base-ten blocks.
Subtract. Regroup if you need to.

1.

tens	ones
4	13
5̶	3̶
−	6
4	7

tens	ones
3	11
4̶	1̶
−	4
3	7

tens	ones
5	15
6̶	5̶
−	7
5	8

tens	ones
1	11
2̶	1̶
−	3
1	8

2.

tens	ones
8	7
−	5
8	2

tens	ones
1	12
2̶	2̶
−	4
1	8

tens	ones
7	16
8̶	6̶
−	8
7	8

tens	ones
3	18
4̶	8̶
−	9
3	9

3.

tens	ones
2	14
3̶	4̶
−	7
2	7

tens	ones
6	15
7̶	5̶
−	8
6	7

tens	ones
5	11
6̶	1̶
−	4
5	7

tens	ones
4	5
−	2
4	3

▶ **Problem Solving**

Subtract. Regroup if you need to.

4. Kim had 86 marbles. She gave 9 marbles to James. How many marbles does Kim have left?

___77___ marbles

Two-Digit Subtraction

Use Workmat 3 and base-ten blocks.
Subtract. Regroup if you need to.

1.

tens	ones
4	12
5̶	2̶
− 2	7
2	5

tens	ones
8	15
9̶	5̶
− 4	6
4	9

tens	ones
8	2
− 7	1
1	1

tens	ones
5	16
6̶	6̶
− 1	9
4	7

2.

tens	ones
8	15
9̶	5̶
− 2	8
6	7

tens	ones
5	17
6̶	7̶
−	8
5	9

tens	ones
7	7
− 1	6
6	1

tens	ones
6	18
7̶	8̶
− 5	9
1	9

3.

tens	ones
8	17
9̶	7̶
− 1	8
7	9

tens	ones
8	14
9̶	4̶
−	6
8	8

tens	ones
5	11
6̶	1̶
− 2	7
3	4

tens	ones
5	4
− 4	3
1	1

▶ **Problem Solving**

4. Justin counted 24 drums and
9 trumpets on a store shelf.
How many more drums than
trumpets did Justin count?

___15___ drums

Practicing Two-Digit Subtraction

Subtract.

1.

$$\begin{array}{r} \overset{1}{\cancel{2}}\overset{17}{\cancel{7}} \\ -\ \ 8 \\ \hline 1\ 9 \end{array}$$

$$\begin{array}{r} 7\ 4 \\ -1\ 2 \\ \hline 6\ 2 \end{array}$$

$$\begin{array}{r} \overset{8}{\cancel{9}}\overset{14}{\cancel{4}} \\ -2\ 5 \\ \hline 6\ 9 \end{array}$$

$$\begin{array}{r} \overset{5}{\cancel{6}}\overset{13}{\cancel{3}} \\ -4\ 7 \\ \hline 1\ 6 \end{array}$$

2.

$$\begin{array}{r} \overset{2}{\cancel{3}}\overset{11}{\cancel{1}} \\ -1\ 9 \\ \hline 1\ 2 \end{array}$$

$$\begin{array}{r} \overset{5}{\cancel{6}}\overset{13}{\cancel{3}} \\ -5\ 6 \\ \hline 7 \end{array}$$

$$\begin{array}{r} \overset{5}{\cancel{6}}\overset{15}{\cancel{5}} \\ -2\ 6 \\ \hline 3\ 9 \end{array}$$

$$\begin{array}{r} 7\ 3 \\ -5\ 1 \\ \hline 2\ 2 \end{array}$$

3.

$$\begin{array}{r} 1\ 6 \\ -1\ 4 \\ \hline 2 \end{array}$$

$$\begin{array}{r} \overset{3}{\cancel{4}}\overset{11}{\cancel{1}} \\ -1\ 7 \\ \hline 2\ 4 \end{array}$$

$$\begin{array}{r} \overset{5}{\cancel{6}}\overset{16}{\cancel{6}} \\ -1\ 8 \\ \hline 4\ 8 \end{array}$$

$$\begin{array}{r} \overset{4}{\cancel{5}}\overset{12}{\cancel{2}} \\ -4\ 9 \\ \hline 3 \end{array}$$

4.

$$\begin{array}{r} \overset{6}{\cancel{7}}\overset{16}{\cancel{6}} \\ -6\ 7 \\ \hline 9 \end{array}$$

$$\begin{array}{r} \overset{4}{\cancel{5}}\overset{12}{\cancel{2}} \\ -\ \ 4 \\ \hline 4\ 8 \end{array}$$

$$\begin{array}{r} \overset{7}{\cancel{8}}\overset{11}{\cancel{1}} \\ -1\ 2 \\ \hline 6\ 9 \end{array}$$

$$\begin{array}{r} 9\ 1 \\ -2\ 1 \\ \hline 7\ 0 \end{array}$$

▶ **Problem Solving**

5. Marvin hit 26 golf balls. He lost 8 of them. How many golf balls does Marvin have left?

_18_ golf balls

Using Addition to Check Subtraction

Subtract.
Add to check.

1.

$$\begin{array}{r} 56 \\ -11 \\ \hline 45 \end{array}$$
$$\begin{array}{r} 45 \\ +11 \\ \hline 56 \end{array}$$
$$\begin{array}{r} 34 \\ -16 \\ \hline 18 \end{array}$$
$$\begin{array}{r} 18 \\ +16 \\ \hline 34 \end{array}$$
$$\begin{array}{r} 19 \\ -11 \\ \hline 8 \end{array}$$
$$\begin{array}{r} 8 \\ +11 \\ \hline 19 \end{array}$$

2.

$$\begin{array}{r} 78 \\ -29 \\ \hline 49 \end{array}$$
$$\begin{array}{r} 49 \\ +29 \\ \hline 78 \end{array}$$
$$\begin{array}{r} 94 \\ -57 \\ \hline 37 \end{array}$$
$$\begin{array}{r} 37 \\ +57 \\ \hline 94 \end{array}$$
$$\begin{array}{r} 47 \\ -16 \\ \hline 31 \end{array}$$
$$\begin{array}{r} 31 \\ +16 \\ \hline 47 \end{array}$$

3.

$$\begin{array}{r} 41 \\ -17 \\ \hline 24 \end{array}$$
$$\begin{array}{r} 24 \\ +17 \\ \hline 41 \end{array}$$
$$\begin{array}{r} 37 \\ -15 \\ \hline 22 \end{array}$$
$$\begin{array}{r} 22 \\ +15 \\ \hline 37 \end{array}$$
$$\begin{array}{r} 85 \\ -48 \\ \hline 37 \end{array}$$
$$\begin{array}{r} 37 \\ +48 \\ \hline 85 \end{array}$$

4.

$$\begin{array}{r} 99 \\ -27 \\ \hline 72 \end{array}$$
$$\begin{array}{r} 72 \\ +27 \\ \hline 99 \end{array}$$
$$\begin{array}{r} 85 \\ -76 \\ \hline 9 \end{array}$$
$$\begin{array}{r} 9 \\ +76 \\ \hline 85 \end{array}$$
$$\begin{array}{r} 51 \\ -24 \\ \hline 27 \end{array}$$
$$\begin{array}{r} 27 \\ +24 \\ \hline 51 \end{array}$$

▶ **Problem Solving**

5. Chi has 7 dimes and 5 pennies.
He trades 1 dime for 10 pennies.
How many dimes and pennies
does Chi now have?

___6___ dimes ___15___ pennies

Problem Solving • Choose the Operation

Work with a partner. Use coins. Add or subtract.
Give your partner the exact amount.

1. How much money would you need to buy a ⊛ and a 🐚 ?

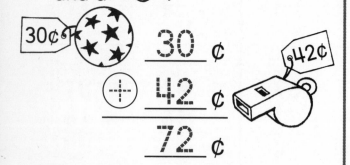

30¢

$$
\begin{array}{r}
\underline{30}\ ¢ \\
\oplus\ \underline{42}\ ¢ \\
\hline
\underline{72}\ ¢
\end{array}
$$

42¢

2. You have 75¢. You buy a ✏️. How much money do you have left?

You have $\underline{75}$ ¢

$$
\begin{array}{r}
\ominus\ \underline{48}\ ¢ \\
\hline
\underline{27}\ ¢
\end{array}
$$

48¢

3. You have 94¢. You buy a ✈️. How much money do you have left?

You have $\underline{94}$ ¢

$$
\begin{array}{r}
\ominus\ \underline{85}\ ¢ \\
\hline
\underline{9}\ ¢
\end{array}
$$

85¢

4. How much money would you need to buy a 🎈 and a 🥁 ?

35¢

$$
\begin{array}{r}
\underline{35}\ ¢ \\
\oplus\ \underline{63}\ ¢ \\
\hline
\underline{98}\ ¢
\end{array}
$$

63¢

5. How much money would you need to buy a 📖 and 🖌️ ?

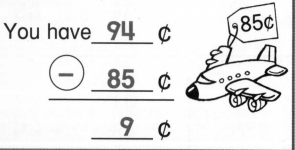

55¢

$$
\begin{array}{r}
\underline{55}\ ¢ \\
\oplus\ \underline{29}\ ¢ \\
\hline
\underline{84}\ ¢
\end{array}
$$

29¢

6. You have 64¢. You buy a bag of 🍿. How much money do you have left?

You have $\underline{64}$ ¢

45¢

$$
\begin{array}{r}
\ominus\ \underline{45}\ ¢ \\
\hline
\underline{19}\ ¢
\end{array}
$$

Harcourt Brace School Publishers

Tally Tables

Use the picture to fill in the tally marks.
Use the table to answer the questions.

Dogs	
black	IIII
white	II
spotted	I

1. How many white dogs are there?   __2__ white dogs

2. Are there more black dogs
   or white dogs?

   _____
   - - - - - - - - - - - - - -
   black dogs

3. How many dogs are there in all?   __7__ dogs

4. How many black dogs are there?   __4__ black dogs

▶ **Problem Solving**

Use the table. Draw a picture and
write a number sentence to answer
the question.

5. How many more spotted dogs
   would it take to equal the
   black dogs?

   __3__ more spotted dogs

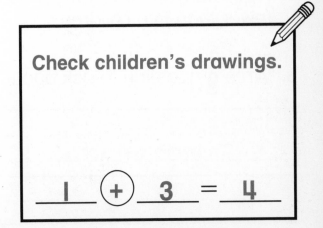

Check children's drawings.

__1__ (+) __3__ = __4__

Name _____

Problem Solving • Use a Table

This table shows the number of children
who chose each flavor of ice cream.

chocolate	卌 I
vanilla	IIII
strawberry	III
cherry	IIII
banana	II

1. Write a title for the table.

Answers will vary.

2. How many children chose
   banana?

   ___2___ children

3. Which flavor was chosen by the
   most children?

   _____
   - - - - - - - - - - - - - - - -
   ___chocolate___

4. How many more children chose
   chocolate than vanilla?

   ___2___ more children

5. How many flavors were chosen by
   fewer than five children?

   ___4___ flavors

6. Write a question to ask about this table.

   _____
   - - - - - - - - - - - - - - - -
   ___Answers will vary.___
   _____
   - - - - - - - - - - - - - - - -
   _____

Harcourt Brace School Publishers

Taking a Survey

Ask 10 classmates these questions.
Fill in tally marks.
Then answer the questions at the bottom.

Answers will vary.

1. Which of these sports do you like the best?

baseball	
soccer	
basketball	
swimming	

2. Which is your favorite season?

spring	
summer	
fall	
winter	

3. Which sport is the favorite?

_____
- - - - - - - - - - - - - - - -
_____

4. How many children like summer the best? _____ children

▶ Problem Solving

The table shows 10 children's favorite meal.
Write a number sentence to answer the question.

5. How many more children like lunch than dinner the best?

__5__ ⊝ __2__ = __3__

__3__ more children

Which is your favorite meal?	
breakfast	|||
lunch	ⴕ⎮
dinner	||

Harcourt Brace School Publishers

Name_____

Comparing Data in Tables

Use the tables to answer the questions.

Favorite Animals Mr. Donaldson's Class	
dog	|||| |||| ||
cat	|||| |||
tiger	||||
bird	||
horse	||||

Favorite Animals Ms. Rubiella's Class	
dog	|||| ||||
cat	|||| |||
tiger	|||
bird	||||
horse	||||	

1. Which animal got the same number of votes in each class?

   cat

2. In which class do more children like horses?

   Ms. Rubiella's

3. In which class do fewer children like birds?

   Mr. Donaldson's

4. Which animals got the same number of votes in Mr. Donaldson's class?

   tiger and horse

5. Do more people in Ms. Rubiella's class like dogs and cats or tigers and horses?

   dogs and cats

▶ **Problem Solving**

Use the tables. Circle the question that you **can** answer.

6. (How many children in the two classes like tigers the best?)

   How many more children in Ms. Rubiella's class like rabbits than birds the best?

Name _____

LESSON
15.1

Picture Graphs

Use the graph to answer the questions.

Favorite Fruit	
apple	🍎🍎🍎🍎🍎🍎🍎🍎🍎🍎
pear	🍐🍐
orange	🍊🍊🍊🍊
banana	🍌🍌🍌🍌🍌🍌🍌

1. Which fruit is liked by the most people? **apple**

2. Which fruit is liked by the fewest people? **pear**

3. How many more people like apples than oranges? __6__ more people

4. How many fewer people like pears than bananas? __5__ fewer people

▶ **Problem Solving**

Use the graph. Write a number sentence to answer the question.

5. How many people like apples and bananas?

   __17__ people

   __10__ (+) __7__ = __17__

Harcourt Brace School Publishers

ON MY OWN P83

Pictographs

Use the graph to answer the questions.

Children Who Ride the Bus to School	
Room 201	☺ ☺ ☺ ☺
Room 202	☺ ☺ ☺ ☺ ☺
Room 203	☺ ☺

Each ☺ stands for 2 children.

1. How many children ride the bus in Room 203?

   ___4___ children

2. Which room has the fewest children who ride the bus?

   Room 203

3. How many more children in Room 202 ride the bus than in Room 203?

   ___6___ more children

4. How many children in Rooms 201 and 202 ride the bus?

   __18__ children

▶ **Problem Solving**

Use the graph. Draw a picture and write a number sentence.

5. There are 20 children in Room 202. How many children do not ride the bus?

   __10__ children

Check children's drawings.

__20__ ⊖ __10__ = __10__

Harcourt Brace School Publishers

Horizontal Bar Graphs

Use the tally table to fill in the graph.

Our Favorite Cakes	
chocolate	ⵌⵌ ⵌⵌ
vanilla	ⵌⵌ II
lemon	III
pineapple	ⵌⵌ

Our Favorite Cakes

	0	1	2	3	4	5	6	7	8	9	10
chocolate											
vanilla											
lemon											
pineapple											

1. Which cake is liked by the fewest people? _lemon_

2. Which cake is liked by the most people? _chocolate_

3. How many more people like
   chocolate cake than pineapple cake?   _5_ more people

▶ Problem Solving

Use the bar graph. Circle the question you **can not** answer.

4. How many people voted for
   their favorite cake?

   How many people like
   carrot cake?

Problem Solving • Make a Graph

Ask 10 people which color they like the best.

1. Fill in the tally table to show their answers.

Colors We Like	
red	Answers will vary.
green	
blue	
yellow	

2. Use the tally table to fill in the graph.

Colors We Like										
<u>red</u>										
<u>green</u>										
<u>blue</u>										
<u>yellow</u>										

0   1   2   3   4   5   6   7   8   9   10

Answers will vary.

3. How many people like green the best?   _____ people

_____

4. Which color do the most people like?   - - - - - - - - - - - -

_____

5. Which color do the fewest people like?   - - - - - - - - - - - -

_____

6. How many people in all like blue and red?   _____ people

Harcourt Brace School Publishers

Certain or Impossible

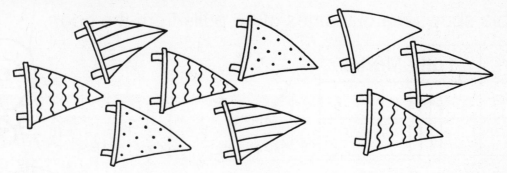

Use the picture.
Circle the groups of flags that you are certain to find on the wall.
Cross out the groups of flags that are impossible to find on the wall.

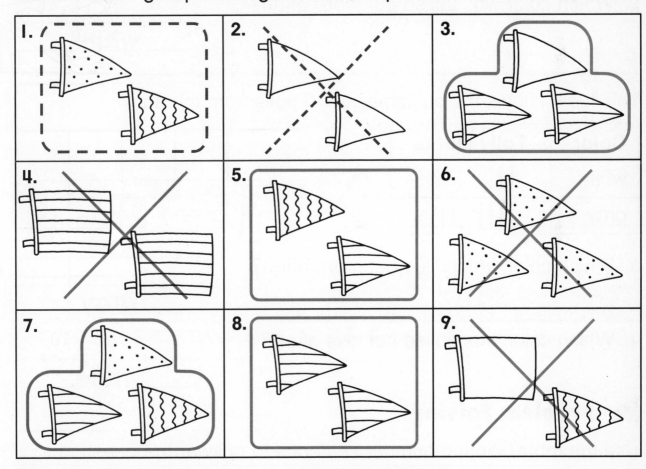

▶ **Problem Solving**

Write **Yes** or **No.**

10. Can you take 2 ⬤ from this box?

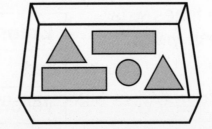

No

Interpreting Outcomes of Games

This table shows the outcomes of 10 pulls from the bag.

Color	Tally Marks
white	卌 I
gray	IIII

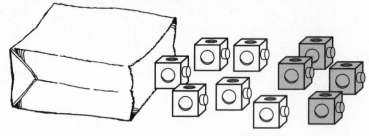

1. Which color was pulled out less often?

_____
gray

2. Which color was pulled out more often?

_____
white

This table shows the outcomes of 10 pulls from the bag.

Color	Tally Marks
white	II
gray	卌 III

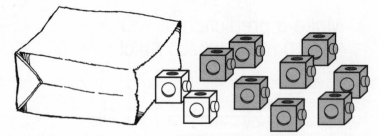

3. Which color was pulled out more often?

_____
gray

4. Which color was pulled out less often?

_____
white

 Problem Solving

Use the table. Write a number sentence to answer the question.

5. How many more times was red pulled out than yellow?

Color	Tally Marks
red	卌 卌 I
yellow	卌

__11__ ⊖ __5__ = __6__

Harcourt Brace School Publishers

Most Likely

You will need: 8 blue tiles, 4 red tiles, 3 yellow tiles, 1 bag

Color	Tally Marks
blue	_Answers will vary._
red	
yellow	

Part 1

1. Put all the tiles in the bag. Pull out 1 tile.

2. Make a tally mark to show which color you pulled out. Put the tile back into the bag. Shake. Do this 9 more times.

3. Make a prediction. If you do this 10 more times, which color do you think you will pull out most often?

   _____
   _____
   Answers will vary.

Part 2

4. Do this 10 more times. Make a tally mark each time.

5. Which color tile did you pull out most often?

   _____
   _____
   Answers will vary.

6. Why do you think this happened?

   _____
   Answers will vary.
   _____
   Answers will vary.

▶ Problem Solving

Kathy pulled a blue tile from her bag 11 times. She pulled a red tile 7 times and a yellow tile 2 times.

7. Which color tile do you think there is most of in her bag?

   _____
   _____
   Answers will vary.

8. Draw a picture to show what might be in her bag.

Less Likely

1. Color the cubes. Make a prediction.
Circle the bag that you think you will pull
green from less often.

Answers may vary.

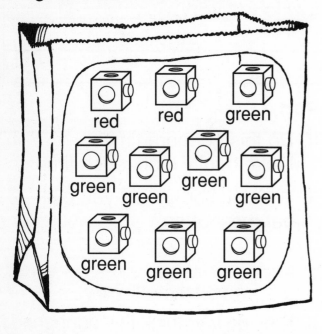

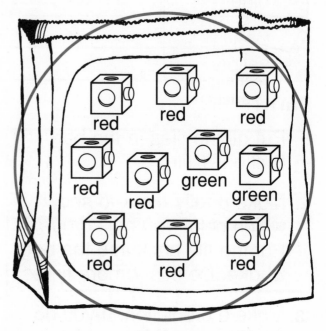

2. Pull out 1 cube 10 times. Make a tally mark each time.

Color	Tally Marks
red	**Answers will vary.**
green	

Color	Tally Marks
red	**Answers will vary.**
green	

3. Was your prediction correct? _____

_ _

Answers will vary.

▶ Problem Solving

4. Color the spinner that
you are certain will stop
on red if you spin the
pointer 10 times.

Check children's work.

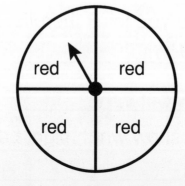

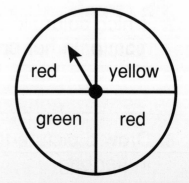

Harcourt Brace School Publishers

Name _____

Identifying Solids

Color the figures that are the same shape.

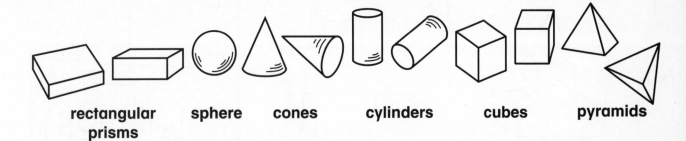

rectangular prisms   sphere   cones   cylinders   cubes   pyramids

1. Check children's coloring.

2.

3.

4.

5.

6.

▶ **Problem Solving**

7. Circle the figures that are alike in two ways.

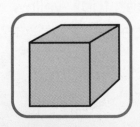 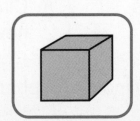 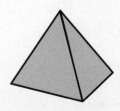

Sorting Solid Figures

Circle the solid figure that is missing.

1.
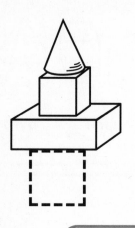
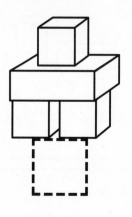

2.
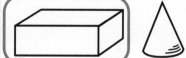

3.
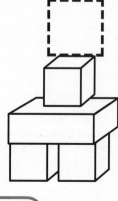

4.
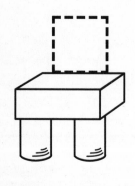

5.
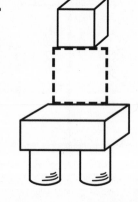

6.
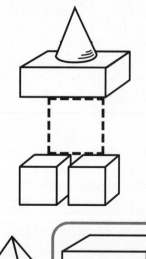

 Problem Solving

7. Circle the figure that has no flat faces.

 sphere   cone   cylinder

8. Circle the figures that have all flat faces.

sphere   cube   rectangular prism

Problem Solving • Look for a Pattern

There is a mistake in each pattern.
Cross out the mistake.
Circle the solid figure that belongs.

1.

2.

3.

4.

5.

6.

Making Plane Figures

Circle the plane figure you can
trace from the solid figure.

1.

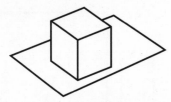

2.

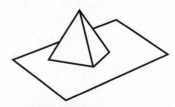

3.

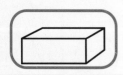

4.

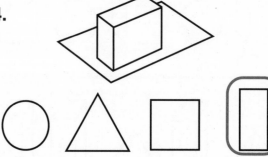

Circle the solid figure you can
use to trace the faces.

5.

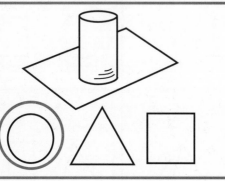

6.

7.

8.

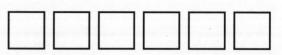

Plane Figures

1. Color the triangles green .

Color the rectangles blue .

Color the squares red .

Check children's coloring.

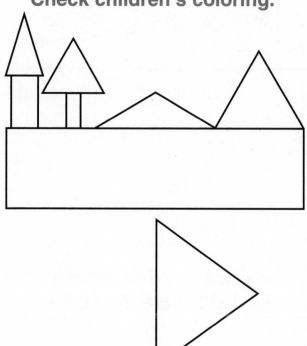

2. Color the circles purple .

Color the squares yellow .

Color the triangles orange .

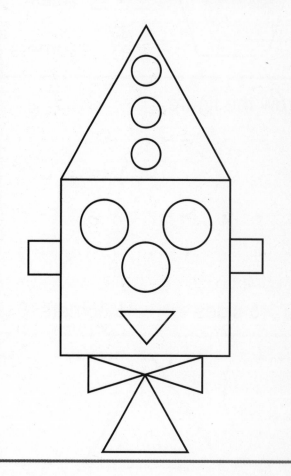

▶ **Problem Solving**

3. Cross out the figures that are not rectangles.

---

4. Cross out the figures that are not triangles.

Sides and Corners

Write how many sides and corners.

1.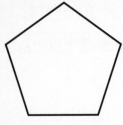

_5_ sides

_5_ corners

2.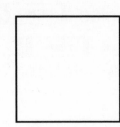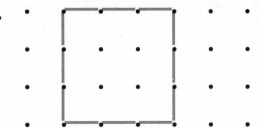

_4_ sides

_4_ corners

Draw the figure.   **Check children's work.**

3.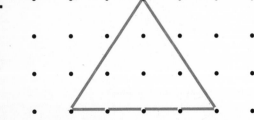

6 sides   6 corners

4.

4 sides   4 corners
All 4 sides are the same.

5.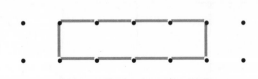

3 sides   3 corners

6.

4 sides   4 corners
2 sides are long. 2 sides are short.

▶ **Problem Solving**

7. What shape has 0 sides
and 0 corners?

_____

circle

8. What shape has 4
equal sides?

_____

square

Harcourt Brace School Publishers

Separating to Make New Figures

Trace the line or lines.
Write how many triangles or squares you made.

1.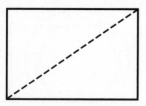

_ _ _ _ _ _ _ _ _ _
2 triangles

2.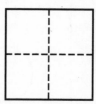

_ _ _ _ _ _ _ _ _ _
4 squares

3.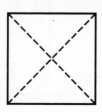

_ _ _ _ _ _ _ _ _ _
4 triangles

4.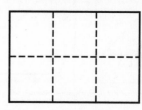

_ _ _ _ _ _ _ _ _ _
6 squares

Draw a line or lines to make the new figures. **Answers will vary.**

5.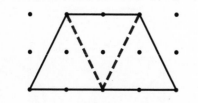

3 triangles

6.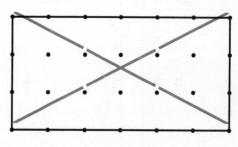

4 triangles

7.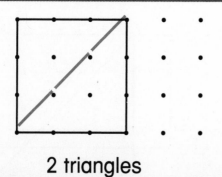

2 triangles

8.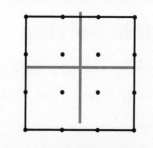

4 squares

Congruent Figures

Circle the figure that fits.

1.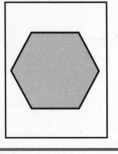

2.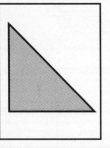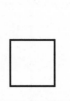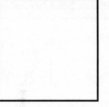

3.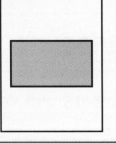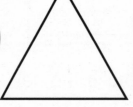

4.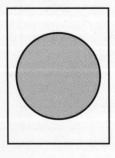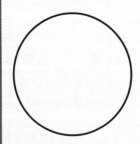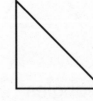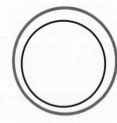

▶ **Problem Solving**

5. How many dots are inside the rectangle but not inside the triangle?

_____**3**_____ dots

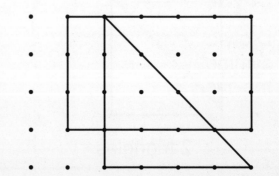

Line of Symmetry

▶ Vocabulary

Find the pictures that have **symmetry.** Draw the line.
Cross out the pictures that do not have symmetry.

1.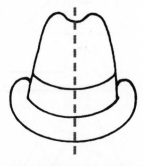

2.

3.

Draw the line of symmetry.

4.

5.

6.

7.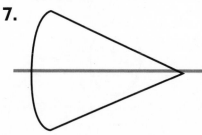

8.

9.

Check children's work.

▶ Problem Solving

10. Draw a figure that has symmetry. Then draw the line.

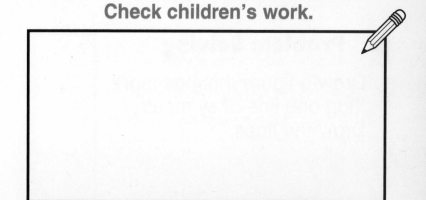

More Symmetry

Draw lines of symmetry. Write how many.

1.

_____

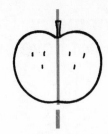
_____

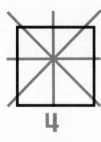
4
_____

2.
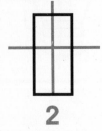
2
_____

1
_____

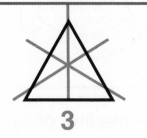
3
_____

3.
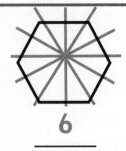
6
_____

1
_____

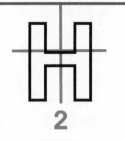
2
_____

4.
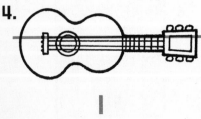
1
_____

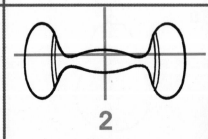
2
_____

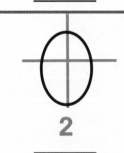
2
_____

Check children's work.

▶ **Problem Solving**

5. Draw a figure that has more than one line of symmetry. Draw the lines.

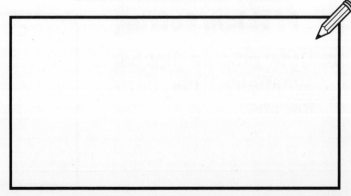

Harcourt Brace School Publishers

Name _____

Moving Figures

Use a punch-out trapezoid.
Put the trapezoid on top of the first one.
Make it fit on top of the second one.
Circle turn or flip to tell how you moved it.

1.

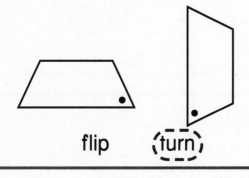

flip   (turn)

2.

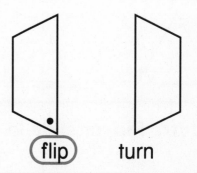

(flip)   turn

3.

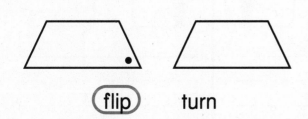

(flip)   turn

4.

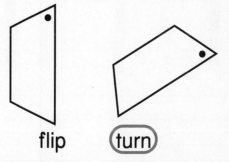

flip   (turn)

5.

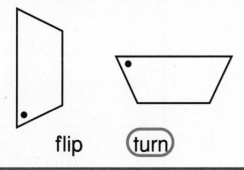

flip   (turn)

6.

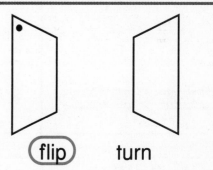

(flip)   turn

▶ **Problem Solving**

7. How would you move this triangle to make it fit in the puzzle?

flip   (turn)

Name _____

More About Moving Figures

Use a punch-out triangle.
Put your triangle on top of the first one.
Slide it to fit on top of the second triangle.   **Check children's work.**
Trace the figure. Draw the dot.

I.    2.

Write **turn**, **flip**, or **slide** to name the move.

3.

		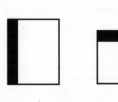

slide	**flip**	**turn**

4.

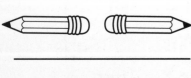	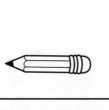	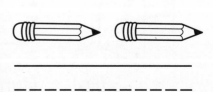
	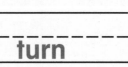	
flip/turn	**turn**	**slide**

▶ **Problem Solving**

5. How would you move this
   triangle to make it fit in
   this puzzle?

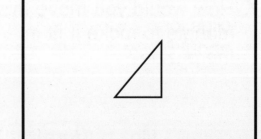

   turn   (flip)   turn

Harcourt Brace School Publishers

Using Nonstandard Units

Use paper clips to measure.
About how many paper clips long is each feather?

1.

about ___3___ paper clips

2.

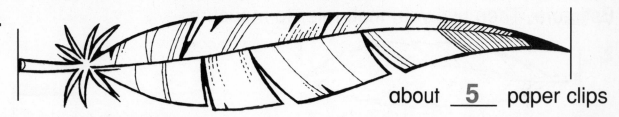

about ___5___ paper clips

3.

about ___2___ paper clips

4.

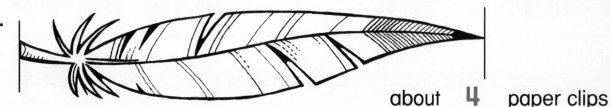

about ___4___ paper clips

▶ **Problem Solving**

Draw a picture to compare and solve.

5. Dwayne's red pencil is about 8 paper clips long. Roberto's green pencil is about 5 paper clips long.
About how many paper clips longer is the red pencil?

about ___3___ paper clips

Name _____

LESSON
20.2

Measuring with Inch Units

▶ **Vocabulary**

Circle the piece of string that shows one **inch.**

I.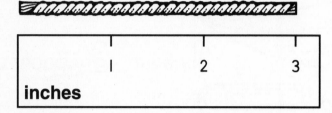

Estimate. Then use your inch ruler to measure.

2.

Estimate _____ inches   Measure __3__ inches

3.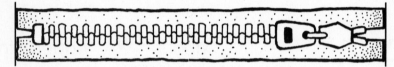

Estimate _____ inches   Measure __4__ inches

4.

Estimate _____ inches   Measure __6__ inches

▶ **Problem Solving**

Use your inch ruler.
Draw the shape.

5. I have 4 sides.
Each side is I inch long.

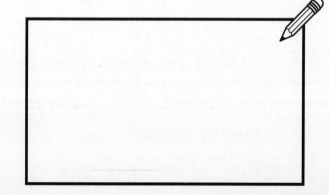

Harcourt Brace School Publishers

Using an Inch Ruler

Work with a partner. Use an inch ruler.
Find these objects.
Write the length.

Answers will vary.

I. crayon

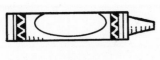

about _____ inches

2. book

about _____ inches

3. scissors

about _____ inches

4. glue

about _____ inches

5. tape

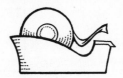

about _____ inches

6. eraser

about _____ inches

▶ **Problem Solving**

Find two more objects in the classroom to measure.
Write the name of the object and how long it is.
Then answer the question.

Answers will vary.

Object	How Long
7. _____	about _____ inches
8. _____	about _____ inches
9. Which object is longer?	_____

Foot

Look around the playground.
Draw pictures of things that are less than,
the same as, and more than 1 foot.
Draw two or more pictures for each.

Less Than	Same As	More Than
	Pictures will vary.	

▶ **Problem Solving**

Draw a picture to solve.

Jan has a red book, a blue book, and
a green book. The red book is longer
than the green book. The blue book
is shorter than the green one.
Which book is the longest?

_____

_____

_____ **red** _____ book

Problem Solving • Guess and Check

Guess the length of the worm. To check, put yarn along the worm and measure the yarn.

Guess.	Check.
1. _____ inches	**4** inches
2. _____ inches	**7** inches
3. _____ inches	**2** inches
4. _____ inches	**5** inches
5. _____ inches	**1** inch
6. _____ inches	**3** inches
7. _____ inches	**6** inches

Centimeters

▶ Vocabulary

Circle the nail that is about 1 **centimeter** long.

1.

Use a centimeter ruler to draw lines.
Start your lines at the dots.

2.   6 centimeters   •- - - - - - - - - - - - - - -

3.   4 centimeters   •   **Check children's work.**

4.   2 centimeters   •

5.   8 centimeters   •

6.   11 centimeters   •

7.   5 centimeters   •

▶ Problem Solving

Use a centimeter ruler.
Draw a line to solve.

8. Kevin has a paper clip that is
   2 centimeters long and one that is
   3 centimeters long. If he connects the
   paper clips, how many centimeters
   long will the two clips be?

   ___5___ centimeters

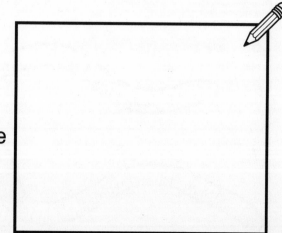

Harcourt Brace School Publishers

Decimeters

▶ **Vocabulary**

How many centimeters equal 1 **decimeter**? Circle the answer.

1. ⑩   1   9

2. Measure these candles with a centimeter ruler.
   Color red the ones that are 1 decimeter tall.

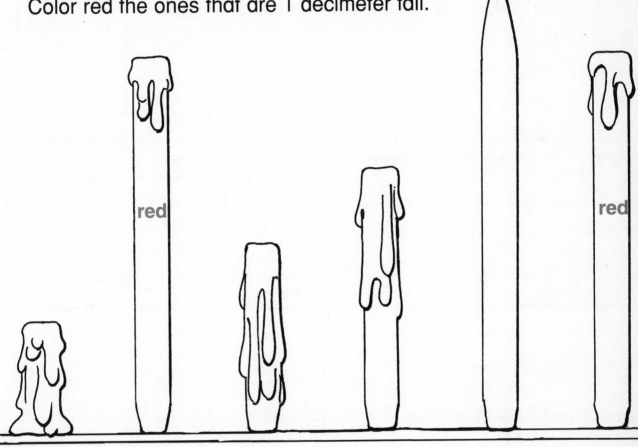

 Problem Solving

Use a centimeter ruler and paper.
Draw a picture to solve.

3. Sam's rope is 2 decimeters long.
   He cuts off 10 centimeters.
   How long is his rope now?

   __10__ centimeters   __1__ decimeter

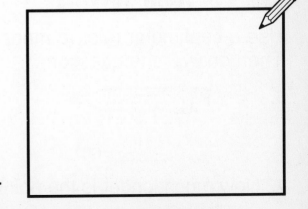

Exploring Perimeter

▶ **Vocabulary**

What word means the same as **the distance around something**?
Circle the word.

1.   centimeter      decimeter

Measure each side. Write how many centimeters.
Then write how many centimeters around the figure.

2.

__3__ + __3__ + __3__ + __3__ = __12__ centimeters

3.

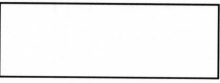

__6__ + __2__ + __6__ + __2__ = __16__ centimeters

4.

__4__ + __5__ + __6__ = __15__
centimeters

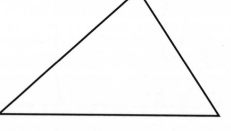

▶ **Problem Solving**

Use a centimeter ruler to measure each object.
Then answer the question.

5.

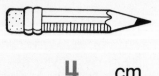

__4__ cm

6.

__7__ cm

7. How much longer is the paintbrush than the pencil? __3__ cm

Harcourt Brace School Publishers

Problem Solving • Guess and Check

Use 1-inch squares. How many 1-inch squares will
fit in the figure? Write your guess.
Then use the squares to check.

1.

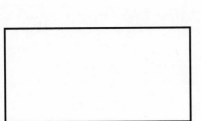

Guess. _____ squares

Check. __2__ squares

2.

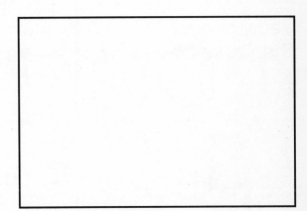

Guess. _____ squares

Check. __6__ squares

3.

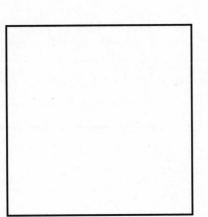

Guess. _____ squares

Check. __4__ squares

4.

Guess. _____ squares

Check. __9__ squares

Using Cups, Pints, and Quarts

Color the cups to show how many hold the same amount.

1.

4 cups are colored.

2.

6 cups are colored.

3.

8 cups are colored.

4.

6 cups are colored.

5.

8 cups are colored.

▶ **Problem Solving**

Draw the picture.
Circle the correct answer.

6. Sally's mother bought 1 quart of milk.
Julie's mother bought 3 pints of milk.
Which one bought more milk?

a. Sally's mother   (b. Julie's mother)

Name _____

More and Less than a Pound

Circle how much each object weighs.

1.

(more than 1 pound)

less than 1 pound

2.

more than 1 pound

(less than 1 pound)

3.

(more than 1 pound)

less than 1 pound

4.

more than 1 pound

(less than 1 pound)

5.

(more than 1 pound)

less than 1 pound

6.

more than 1 pound

(less than 1 pound)

7.

(more than 1 pound)

less than 1 pound

8.

(more than 1 pound)

less than 1 pound

9.

more than 1 pound

(less than 1 pound)

▶ Problem Solving

Number the objects in order from lightest to heaviest.
Use **1, 2,** and **3.**

10.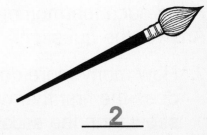

____1____   ____3____   ____2____

Using a Thermometer

Read the temperature. Use a red crayon to color in
the thermometer to show the temperature.

I. 75° F **2.** 50° F **3.** 85° F **4.** 35° F

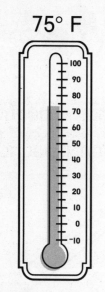 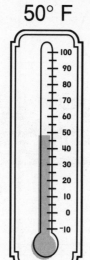 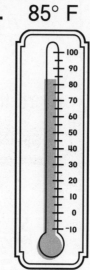 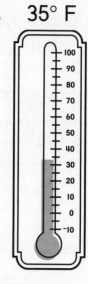

Read the thermometer. Write the temperature.

5.

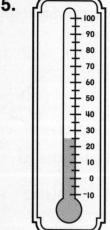

6.

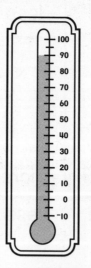

_**25**_ ° F   _**90**_ ° F

▶ **Problem Solving**

Read each thermometer.
Answer the question.

7. How many more degrees
does the first thermometer
show than the second?

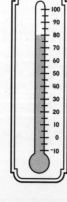 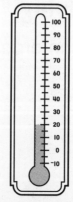

_**60**_ degrees

Harcourt Brace School Publishers

Name _____

Choosing the Appropriate Tool

Write the name of the tool, **cup**, **ruler**, or **thermometer**, you would use.

1. to find out how much milk is in a glass

cup

2. to find out the temperature outside the classroom

thermometer

3. to find out how long a bookshelf is

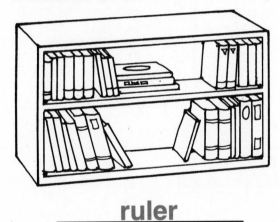

ruler

4. to find out the temperature on a cold day

thermometer

▶ **Problem Solving**

Circle the right tool.

5. Pretend you are making a dog house. Which tool would you use to measure?

cup (ruler) thermometer

Name_____

Halves and Fourths

Color one part 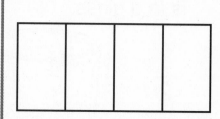.
Circle the fraction.

Check children's coloring.

I.

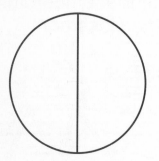

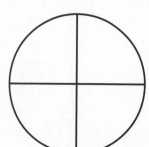

 $\frac{1}{2}$ $\frac{1}{4}$

$\frac{1}{2}$

$\frac{1}{2}$ $\frac{1}{4}$

2.

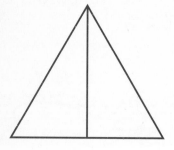

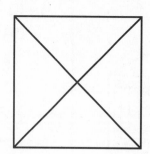

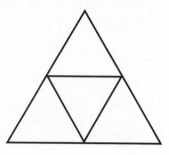

$\frac{1}{2}$ $\frac{1}{4}$

$\frac{1}{2}$

$\frac{1}{2}$

▶ **Problem Solving**

3. Kaley ate $\frac{1}{2}$ of a pizza.

Elliott ate $\frac{1}{4}$ of a pizza.

Circle the one who ate less pizza.

Kaley   Elliott

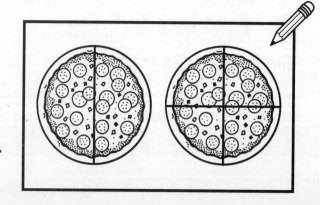

Thirds and Sixths

Color one part 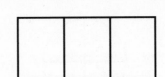 . Circle the fraction. **Check children's coloring.**

1.

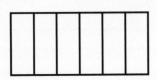

$\frac{1}{2}$ $\frac{1}{3}$ ⟮$\frac{1}{6}$⟯

$\frac{1}{2}$ ⟮$\frac{1}{3}$⟯ $\frac{1}{6}$

⟮$\frac{1}{2}$⟯ $\frac{1}{3}$ $\frac{1}{6}$

2.

$\frac{1}{2}$ ⟮$\frac{1}{3}$⟯ $\frac{1}{6}$

$\frac{1}{2}$ $\frac{1}{3}$ ⟮$\frac{1}{6}$⟯

$\frac{1}{2}$ $\frac{1}{3}$ ⟮$\frac{1}{4}$⟯

3.

$\frac{1}{2}$ $\frac{1}{3}$ ⟮$\frac{1}{4}$⟯

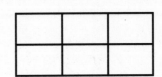

$\frac{1}{2}$ $\frac{1}{3}$ ⟮$\frac{1}{6}$⟯

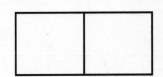

⟮$\frac{1}{2}$⟯ $\frac{1}{3}$ $\frac{1}{6}$

▶ **Problem Solving**

Circle the fraction that is greater.

4.

⟮$\frac{1}{2}$⟯ $\frac{1}{3}$

5.

   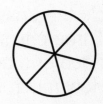

⟮$\frac{1}{3}$⟯ $\frac{1}{6}$

Name _____

More About Fractions

Color to show the fraction. Use red .   **Check children's coloring.**

1.

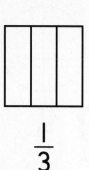

$\dfrac{1}{3}$

$\dfrac{2}{4}$

$\dfrac{2}{3}$

2.

$\dfrac{4}{6}$

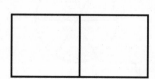

$\dfrac{1}{2}$

$\dfrac{3}{6}$

3.

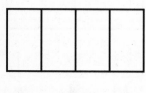

$\dfrac{3}{4}$

$\dfrac{1}{3}$

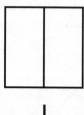

$\dfrac{1}{2}$

▶ **Problem Solving**

Circle the answer.

4. Three children share an apple.
Each one gets an equal share.
How much will each child get?

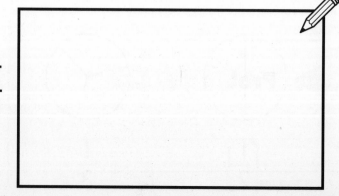

$\boxed{\dfrac{1}{3}}$ $\dfrac{1}{2}$ $\dfrac{1}{6}$

Harcourt Brace School Publishers

Parts of Groups

Circle and color to show the fraction.

Check children's coloring and circles. Sample answers are shown.

1.

$\frac{1}{4}$

2.

$\frac{2}{3}$

3.

$\frac{2}{4}$

4.

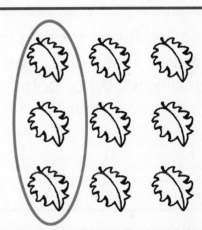

$\frac{1}{3}$

5.

$\frac{1}{6}$

6.

$\frac{1}{2}$

▶ **Problem Solving**

7. There are 8 tulips.

Circle $\frac{1}{4}$ of the group.

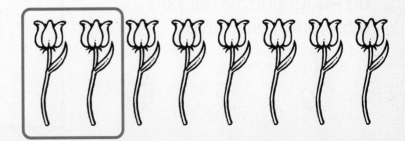

Problem Solving • Make a Model

You will need 12 squares.
Make and draw a model. Then solve.

1. Three children are sharing a set of 12 cubes. Each child has an equal part. What part does one child have?

$\frac{1}{2}$ $\frac{1}{3}$ $\frac{1}{4}$

2. Two children are sharing a set of 8 cubes. Each child has an equal part. What part does one child have?

$\frac{1}{2}$ $\frac{1}{3}$ $\frac{1}{4}$

3. Six children are sharing a set of 12 cubes. Each child has an equal part. What part does one child have?

$\frac{1}{2}$ $\frac{1}{6}$ $\frac{2}{6}$

4. Two children are sharing a set of 6 cubes. Each child has an equal part. What part does one child have?

$\frac{1}{2}$ $\frac{1}{3}$ $\frac{1}{4}$

Harcourt Brace School Publishers

Groups of Hundreds

▶ **Vocabulary**

Write the number.

1. One **hundred** =   __10__ tens

                               __100__ ones

Circle groups of hundreds.
Write how many hundreds, tens, and ones.

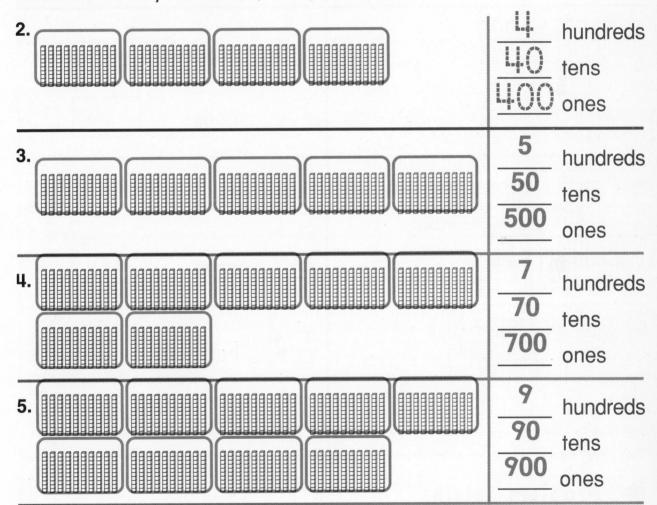

2. __4__ hundreds
__40__ tens
__400__ ones

3. __5__ hundreds
__50__ tens
__500__ ones

4. __7__ hundreds
__70__ tens
__700__ ones

5. __9__ hundreds
__90__ tens
__900__ ones

▶ **Problem Solving**

6. How many hundreds are in 200 ones?   __2__ hundreds

7. How many hundreds are in 60 tens?   __6__ hundreds

Numbers to 500

Use Workmat 5 and base-ten blocks.
Write how many hundreds, tens, and ones.
Then write the number.

1. _4_ hundreds _2_ tens

_6_ ones **426**

2. _1_ hundred _5_ tens

_3_ ones **153**

3. _3_ hundreds _7_ tens

_9_ ones **379**

4. _2_ hundreds _3_ tens

_1_ one **231**

▶ Problem Solving

Write how many hundreds, tens, and ones.

5. 409 = _4_ hundreds _0_ tens _9_ ones

6. 263 = _2_ hundreds _6_ tens _3_ ones

Harcourt Brace School Publishers

Numbers to 1,000

Write the number.

1. 7 hundreds   2 ones   4 tens   =   <u>742</u>

2. 9 ones   5 hundreds   3 tens   =   <u>539</u>

3. 6 ones   7 tens   2 hundreds   =   <u>276</u>

4. 4 tens   5 ones   6 hundreds   =   <u>645</u>

5. 8 hundreds   2 ones   4 tens   =   <u>842</u>

6. 1 one   1 hundred   2 tens   =   <u>121</u>

7. 2 hundreds   0 tens   2 ones   =   <u>202</u>

▶ Problem Solving

Write the number.

8. Andy has 7 ones,
6 hundreds, and 0 tens.
What number is he showing?

<u>607</u>

9. Patty has 9 tens,
2 hundreds, and 3 ones.
What number is she showing?

<u>293</u>

Use a Model

Look at the model. Circle the number that is shown.

1.

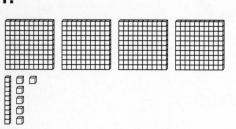

316   (416)   216

2.

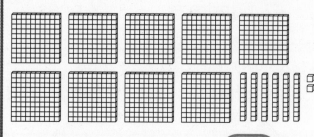

860   862   (962)

3.

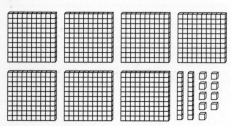

629   529   (729)

4.

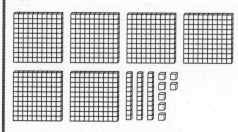

437   (637)   537

5.

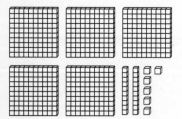

622   525   (526)

6.

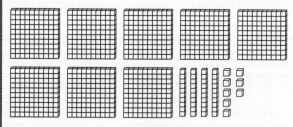

488   (848)   884

▶ **Problem Solving**

7. Write the number that is
10 greater than 271.

_281_

8. Write the number that is
100 greater than 721.

_821_

Building $1.00

▶ Vocabulary

Circle the answer.

1. **One dollar** =   10 pennies   (100 pennies)

Use Workmat 4 and coins.
Show other ways to make $1.00. Write how many.

Answers will vary.

2.	1	1	1	2	5
3.					
4.					
5.					
6.					

▶ Problem Solving

Circle the coins that show the same amount.

7.

Name _____

Greater Than

Compare the two numbers. Circle the number that is greater.

1.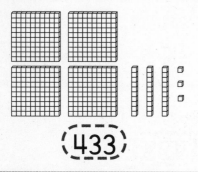

(433)   334

2.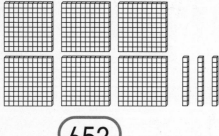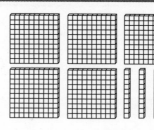

(652)   562

3. 719	(917)	**4.** 202	(220)
5. (400)	399	**6.** 515	(550)
7. (895)	859	**8.** 700	(701)

▶ **Problem Solving**

9. Terry has 105 puzzle pieces. Leticia has 150. Who has the greater number of puzzle pieces?

____**Leticia**____

10. Matthew has 200 marbles. Amy has 210 marbles. Who has the greater number of marbles?

____**Amy**____

Less Than

Compare the two numbers. Circle the number that is less.

1.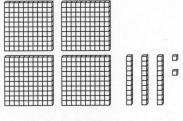

432

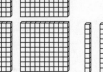

(423)

2.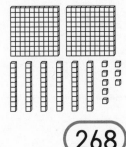

(268)

269

3.	(745)	754	4.	(363)	633
5.	524	(521)	6.	(118)	181
7.	(880)	890	8.	(613)	614

▶ **Problem Solving**

Answers will vary.

Write **greater** or **less**.

9. Is the number of lights in your class greater than or less than the number of windows?

   _____

10. Is the number of boys in your class greater than or less than the number of girls?

   _____

Name _____

Greater Than and Less Than

Complete the statement with **greater** or **less.**
Then write > or < in the circle.

1.
205 is ____less____ than 275.

205 (<) 275

2.
922 is ____less____ than 923.

922 (<) 923

3.
379 is ____greater____ than 319.

379 (>) 319

4.
642 is ____greater____ than 640.

642 (>) 640

5.
505 is ____greater____ than 500.

505 (>) 500

6.
200 is ____less____ than 201.

200 (<) 201

7.
715 is ____less____ than 751.

715 (<) 751

8.
46 is ____less____ than 460.

46 (<) 460

9.
145 is ____greater____ than 140.

145 (>) 140

10.
825 is ____less____ than 826.

825 (<) 826

▶ **Problem Solving**

Look at the number in the boxes.

11. Color green the box with a number
that is less than 480.

| 419 | 491 | 941 |

green

Before, After, and Between

Write the number that is just after,
just before, or between.

205   206   207

1.
205, __206__

2.
__444__, 445

3.
610, __611__, 612

4.
149, __150__

5.
78, __79__, 80

6.
303, __304__

7.
__519__, 520

8.
980, __981__, 982

9.
733, __734__, 735

10.
__516__, 517

11.
136, __137__

12.
42, __43__, 44

▶ **Problem Solving**

13. Leroy and his sister wash 51 forks after their mother's party. There is 1 fork left to wash. How many forks are there in all?

__52__ forks

14. Yoshi has 23 friends at his party. 1 goes home early. How many of Yoshi's friends are still at the party?

__22__ friends

Ordering Sets of Numbers

Write the numbers in order from least to greatest.

1. 419   409   940   941

__409__ ,   __419__ ,   __940__ ,   __941__

2. 276   272   216   220

__216__ ,   __220__ ,   __272__ ,   __276__

3. 140   114   104   144

__104__ ,   __114__ ,   __140__ ,   __144__

4. 959   955   595   949

__595__ ,   __949__ ,   __955__ ,   __959__

5. 383   443   273   353

__273__ ,   __353__ ,   __383__ ,   __443__

6. 614   641   541   647

__541__ ,   __614__ ,   __641__ ,   __647__

▶ **Problem Solving**   **Answers will vary.**

7. Write a number between 300 and 400. _____

Write another number between 300 and 400. _____

Write a number between 200 and 300. _____

Write your three numbers in order from least to greatest.

_____ , _____ , _____

Modeling Addition of Three-Digit Numbers

Use base-ten blocks and Workmat 5.
Add.

1.

hundreds	tens	ones
	1	
2	3	9
+2	0	2
4	4	1

hundreds	tens	ones
	1	
8	0	6
+1	2	7
9	3	3

2.

hundreds	tens	ones
	1	
1	2	9
+4	1	3
5	4	2

hundreds	tens	ones
	1	
2	3	6
+3	1	6
5	5	2

3.

hundreds	tens	ones
	1	
8	0	7
+1	3	4
9	4	1

hundreds	tens	ones
	1	
6	2	8
+1	0	3
7	3	1

▶ Problem Solving

4. Mark has 253 baseball cards. Willa has 272. How many cards do they have in all?

<u>525</u> baseball cards

Adding Three-Digit Numbers

Add.

1.

hundreds	tens	ones
1	1	
4	6	2
+ 4	3	9
9	0	1

hundreds	tens	ones
1	1	
2	4	7
+ 1	7	6
4	2	3

2.

$$\begin{array}{r} \overset{1}{2}07 \\ + 119 \\ \hline 326 \end{array}$$
$$\begin{array}{r} \overset{11}{1}42 \\ + 158 \\ \hline 300 \end{array}$$
$$\begin{array}{r} \overset{1}{8}43 \\ + 109 \\ \hline 952 \end{array}$$
$$\begin{array}{r} \overset{11}{4}01 \\ + 199 \\ \hline 600 \end{array}$$

3.

$$\begin{array}{r} \overset{1}{2}25 \\ + 566 \\ \hline 791 \end{array}$$
$$\begin{array}{r} \overset{1}{4}29 \\ + 117 \\ \hline 546 \end{array}$$
$$\begin{array}{r} \overset{1}{7}56 \\ + 134 \\ \hline 890 \end{array}$$
$$\begin{array}{r} \overset{1}{8}57 \\ + 128 \\ \hline 985 \end{array}$$

4.

$$\begin{array}{r} \overset{1}{4}54 \\ + 36 \\ \hline 490 \end{array}$$
$$\begin{array}{r} \overset{11}{3}01 \\ + 299 \\ \hline 600 \end{array}$$
$$\begin{array}{r} \overset{1}{6}75 \\ + 153 \\ \hline 828 \end{array}$$
$$\begin{array}{r} \overset{1}{5}23 \\ + 407 \\ \hline 930 \end{array}$$

▶ **Problem Solving**

5. There are 237 pennies in one jar and 126 in another jar. How many pennies are there in all?

__363__ pennies

Harcourt Brace School Publishers

Modeling Subtraction of Three-Digit Numbers

Use base-ten blocks and Workmat 5.
Subtract.

1.

hundreds	tens	ones
	2	10
7	3̶	0̶
−4	1	2
3	1	8

hundreds	tens	ones
	8	11
3	9̶	1̶
−2	0	4
1	8	7

2.

hundreds	tens	ones
	1	12
8	2̶	2̶
−1	0	6
7	1	6

hundreds	tens	ones
	4	16
7	5̶	6̶
−2	4	8
5	0	8

3.

hundreds	tens	ones
	2	18
5	3̶	8̶
−1	1	9
4	1	9

hundreds	tens	ones
	2	14
8	3̶	4̶
−	2	7
8	0	7

► **Problem Solving**

4. There are 121 almonds and
102 pecans in the jar. How
many more almonds than
pecans are there?

___19___ more almonds

Subtracting Three-Digit Numbers

Subtract.

1.

hundreds	tens	ones
5	10	
6̸	0̸	6
− 2	5	2
3	5	4

hundreds	tens	ones
7	13	
8̸	3̸	5
− 4	7	2
3	6	3

2.

```
  5 11
  6̸1̸9
− 325
  294
```

```
  4 10
  5̸0̸4
− 182
  322
```

```
  4 15
  6̸5̸5̸
− 147
  508
```

```
  7 12
  8̸2̸4
− 654
  170
```

3.

```
  1 12
  2̸2̸9
−  86
  143
```

```
  6 14
  9̸7̸4̸
− 155
  819
```

```
  3 13
  7̸4̸3
− 716
   27
```

```
  2 10
  3̸0̸3
− 111
  192
```

4.

```
  168
− 138
   30
```

```
  599
− 498
  101
```

```
  5 10
  4̸6̸0̸
− 237
  223
```

```
  8 12
  9̸2̸4̸
− 193
  731
```

▶ **Problem Solving**

5. At the zoo, there are 426 animals and 135 zoo workers. How many more animals than workers are there?

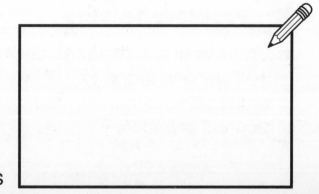

____291____ more animals

Adding and Subtracting Money

Add or subtract.

1.

$2.64 − 1.30 **$1.34**	5 18 $4.6̸8̸ − 1.29 **$3.39**	1 $3.72 + 1.46 **$5.18**	3 15 $5.4̸5̸ − 3.16 **$2.29**

2.

1 $4.56 + 1.07 **$5.63**	1 10 $4.2̸0̸ − 3.19 **$1.01**	1 $3.74 + 2.09 **$5.83**	0 12 $1̸.2̸8̸ − .55 **$ .73**

3.

2 12 $3.3̸2̸ − 2.23 **$1.09**	1 1 $1.59 + 2.68 **$4.27**	1 16 $2̸.6̸9̸ − 1.87 **$ .82**	1 1 $1.12 + .88 **$2.00**

▶ **Problem Solving**

4. Sam has $4.25. Molly has $2.50. How much more money does Sam have than Molly?

$ __1.75__

5. Elijah has $3.20. He spends $2.75 on a toy train. How much money does he have left?

$ __.45__

Adding Equal Groups

Use Workmat 6 and cubes.
Use cubes to show equal groups.
Draw them. Write how many in all.

Check children's work.

I.

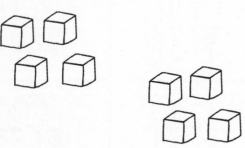

2 groups of 4

$4 + 4 = \underline{8}$

2.

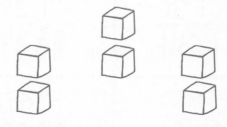

3 groups of 2

$2 + 2 + 2 = \underline{6}$

3.

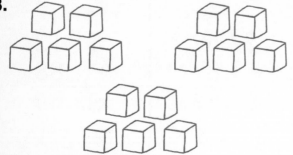

3 groups of 5

$5 + 5 + 5 = \underline{15}$

4.

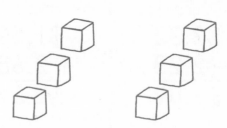

2 groups of 3

$3 + 3 = \underline{6}$

▶ **Problem Solving**

5. Sarah got flowers for her father. She got 3 daisies, 3 lilies, and 3 roses.

Draw a picture to show equal groups of Sarah's flowers. Write a number sentence to show how many flowers Sarah has in all.

$\underline{3 + 3 + 3} = \underline{9}$ flowers

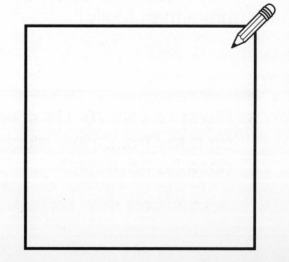

Name _____

Multiplying with 2 and 5

▶ **Vocabulary**

Circle the **sum** . Circle the **product** 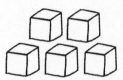.

1.　　4 x 3 = ⑫ blue　　　　4 + 3 = ⑦ red

Write the sum. Then write the product.

2.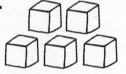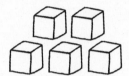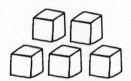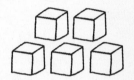

5 + 5 + 5 + 5 = __20__　　　4 x 5 = __20__

3.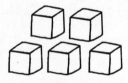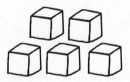

5 + 5 = __10__　　　2 x 5 = __10__

4.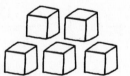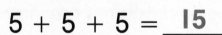

5 + 5 + 5 = __15__　　　3 x 5 = __15__

▶ **Problem Solving**

Draw a picture to solve.

5. There are 2 children. Each child has 3 balloons. How many balloons do they have in all?

____6____ balloons

Multiplying with 3 and 4

Write the multiplication sentence.

1.

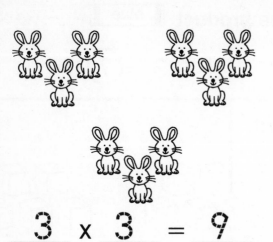

___3___ x ___3___ = ___9___

2.

___2___ x ___3___ = ___6___

3.

___4___ x ___3___ = ___12___

4.

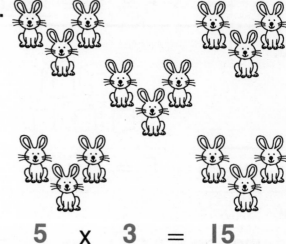

___5___ x ___3___ = ___15___

▶ **Problem Solving**

5. Billy had some marbles. He gave 3 marbles to each of his 3 friends. How many marbles did Billy give away?

Draw a picture. Write the multiplication sentence.

___3___ x ___3___ = ___9___
marbles

Check children's drawings.

Harcourt Brace School Publishers

Problem Solving • Draw a Picture

Draw a picture to solve the problem.
Write the multiplication sentence.

Check children's work.

1. There are 3 squirrels in the yard. Each squirrel has 4 nuts. How many nuts in all do the squirrels have?

   ___3___ x ___4___ = __12__ nuts

2. There are 5 seesaws in the park. Each has 2 children on it. How many children in all are on the seesaws?

   ___5___ x ___2___ = __10__ children

3. There are 2 people getting library books. Each has 4 books. How many books in all are they getting?

   ___2___ x ___4___ = ___8___ books

4. Tommy and his mother go to a movie. Each gets 2 snacks. How many snacks in all do they get?

   ___2___ x ___2___ = ___4___ snacks

Harcourt Brace School Publishers

How Many in Each Group?

Circle equal groups.
Write how many are in each group.

1. 5 equal groups

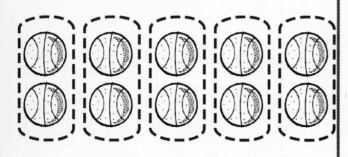

_____2_____ in each group

2. 4 equal groups

_____2_____ in each group

3. 2 equal groups

_____3_____ in each group

4. 3 equal groups

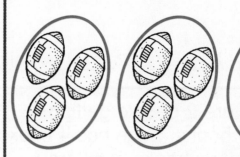

_____3_____ in each group

 Problem Solving

Write how many are in each group.

5. Draw 12 balloons.
   Circle equal groups.

Answers will vary.

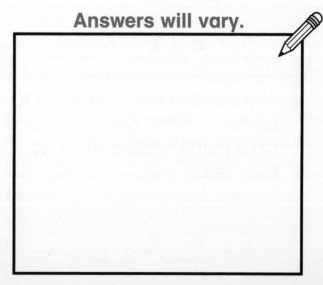

_____ in each group

Harcourt Brace School Publishers

Name _____

LESSON
28.2

How Many Equal Groups?

Circle an equal number in each group.
Write how many groups.

1. groups of 3

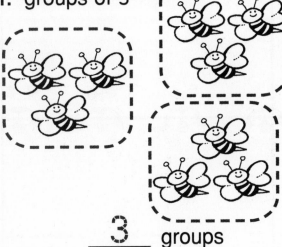

__3__ groups

2. groups of 5

__2__ groups

3. groups of 2

__4__ groups

4. groups of 4

__3__ groups

▶ **Problem Solving**

Draw a picture to solve.

5. How many pairs of socks
   will 10 socks make?

   __5__ pairs of socks

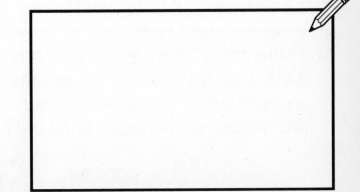

Harcourt Brace School Publishers

ON MY OWN P141

Problem Solving • Draw a Picture

Draw a picture to solve.

1. Debbie gave 9 flowers to 3 friends.
She gave an equal number to
each. How many flowers did each
friend get?

   ___3___ flowers

2. There are 14 stickers. There are
2 children. Each child will get the
same number of stickers. How
many stickers will each child get?

   ___7___ stickers

3. Montel gave 12 baseball cards to
his brother and sister. He gave an
equal number to each. How many
baseball cards did each one get?

   ___6___ baseball cards

4. Sue gave 8 markers to 4 friends.
She gave an equal number to
each. How many markers did
each one get?

   ___2___ markers

5. There are 12 cookies. There are
3 children. Each child will get the
same number of cookies. How
many cookies will each child get?

   ___4___ cookies

Problem Solving • Choose a Strategy

Draw a picture or make a model to solve.

1. Mario and Eric went to the store. They each spent $4.00. How much money did they spend in all?

    $ __8.00__

2. Ty gave 15 pencils to 5 friends. He gave an equal number to each. How many pencils did each friend get?

    __3__ pencils

3. One apple costs 5¢. Dylan has 25¢. How many apples can he buy?

    __5__ apples

4. Tranh gave 6 bottle caps to 2 friends. He gave an equal number to each. How many caps did each friend get?

    __3__ bottle caps

5. Ellen had 111 pennies. She gave her brother 50. How many pennies did she have left?

    __61__ pennies

Harcourt Brace School Publishers